Key Stage 3

Graphic Products

Design & Technology

Stanley Thornes (Publishers) Ltd

Name ....

School ....

Class / Set ....

First published 1998 by
Stanley Thornes (Publishers) Ltd
Ellenborough House
Wellington Street
CHELTENHAM
GL50 1YW

A catalogue record for this book is available from the British Library.

ISBN 0 7487 3511 9

98 99 00 01 02 / 10 9 8 7 6 5 4 3 2 1

Designed and typeset by Carla Turchini
Picture research by John Bailey
Artwork by Anna Braithwaite, Tristram Ariss
Printed and bound in Spain by Mateu Cromo

The publishers would like to thank the following for permission to reproduce photographs or other material:
Adams Picture Library: p. 15 (bottom)
British Nutrition Foundation: p. 12 (bottom)
British Telecom: p. 14 (top)
Electronics Education: p. 64 (top left and bottom)
Ford Motor Company: p. 20 (bottom right)
IKEA: p. 10 (bottom left)
J Sainsbury plc: p. 12 (middle right)
John Birdsall Photography: pp. 41 (right), 42, 55 (right), 56
Martyn Chillmaid: pp. 6, 7, 8 (bottom), 9 (top), 10 (top right and bottom right), 12 (top and middle centre), 16 (top), 17, 37 (left), 38, 43 (left), 44, 47 (right), 49, 51 (left), 52, 57 (left), 58, 61 (right), 63
Moulinex Swan: p. 10 (top left)
Rex Features: pp. 15 (top – Today), 20 (bottom left – El Sport and top), 21 (bottom SIPA-PRESS)
Science Photolibrary: pp. 11 (bottom left – Rosenfeld Images Ltd), (bottom centre – Peter Menzel) (bottom right – Dick Luria), 13 (bottom – Rosenfeld Images Ltd)
Softwood: p. 18 (top)
The Body Shop: p. 14 (middle right)
Theed Axiom Software: p. 18 (middle – Scott Grayson)
Tony Stone Images: p. 9 (middle – Alan Klehr) (bottom – Joe Cornish), 14 (bottom – Peter Cade), 16 (bottom left – Nick Vedros), 20 (bottom centre – Kevin Horan)
Tristram Shepard: p. 21 (top)
Turbocalc: p. 19 (bottom)

On Target has been designed to be used in conjunction with the Key Stage 3 Design & Make IT! Product Design and Food & Textiles Assessment Resource Packs, also published by Stanley Thornes.

The material in **Design & Technology: On Target** is intended as a guide for pupils and parents to the requirements of the National Curriculum.

Teachers will need to plan schemes of work and make their final judgements about pupils' performance with specific reference to the programmes of study and the Attainment Target level statements laid out in the statutory requirements for Design and Technology, as published by HMSO, 1995.

Contents

Introduction

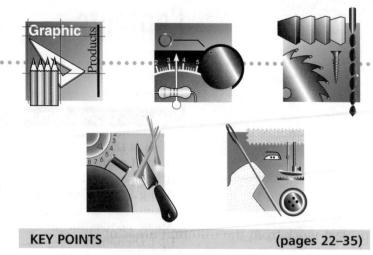

Welcome to *Design and Technology: On Target*. This book will help you to progress through Key Stage 3 and make sure you are well prepared for the start of your GCSE course in Design and Technology. You will need to refer to this book throughout Years 7, 8 and 9.

The book is divided up into three sections.

WHAT IS DESIGN AND TECHNOLOGY? (pages 8–21)

This section explains what 'D&T' is all about, and the various areas of study which are involved. It will help to give you an idea of the sort of work you are likely to be doing in Years 7, 8 and 9, depending on which areas your school offers.

Which areas of Design and Technology does your school offer?

Within D&T in schools there are a number of different areas. These are usually called:

▶ Graphic Products (or just Graphics)
▶ Resistant Materials Technology (or CDT)
▶ Electronic Products / Systems and Control
▶ Food Technology (sometimes called Home Economics)
▶ Textiles Technology (or just Textiles).

Different schools offer different combinations of these areas. Some do all five, but others may only cover one or two. In many schools Resistant Materials, Electronic Products, Systems and Control and Graphic Products are combined together at Key Stage 3. For this reason these areas have been grouped together in this book under the heading of 'Product Design'.

Section 1 also contains a useful 'D&T Dictionary' which explains and illustrates the special words and phrases which are often used in D&T – it's important that you understand what they mean.

KEY POINTS (pages 22–35)

Section 2 provides a useful check-list of all the things you are expected to learn about during the Key Stage. You may find that you are sometimes tested on your knowledge and understanding of the subject. If so you will find it useful to revise from these pages. This section is divided up into a number of topics:

▶ Materials and Components
▶ Systems and Control
▶ Structures
▶ Products and Applications / Quality
▶ Health and Safety.

As you cover the various topics during the Key Stage you can tick them off.

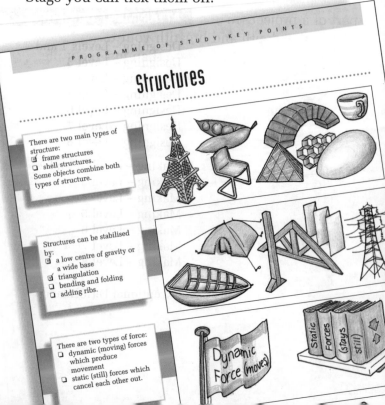

ATTAINMENT TARGETS (pages 36–64)

This section will help you to work out what level you are working at in Designing (AT1) and Making (AT2). It will also help you find out what you need to do to progress to the next level. You can then set yourself some realistic targets to help you achieve this.

Each double page covers one of the Attainment Target levels and provides a check-list of things you need to do to achieve that level. Examples of project work from the different areas of D&T are shown in the pictures across the page.

Each of the two Attainment Targets is divided into different parts, or *aspects*:

AT1: Designing	AT2: Making
● Investigate	● Plan the making
● Have good ideas	● Apply what I know
● Develop my design	● Work with materials
● Apply what I know	● Evaluate my final product
● Evaluate	

The illustrations for each aspect give examples of the sort of work you should be doing to provide evidence of your achievement. Remember, however, that each illustration is only a 'snapshot' of part of a project. To show that you have covered the necessary depth and breadth your design folder will need to contain a lot more than just a couple of sentences and sketches.

Finding your level

First of all you need to find out which level you are currently working at.

▶ If you are in year 7 start by looking at levels 3 and 4.
▶ If you are in year 8 look first at levels 4 and 5.
▶ If you are in year 9 look at levels 5 and 6.

Study the example from the D&T area you are working in at present. For each aspect three examples are given:

▶ one in the area of Product Design
▶ one in the area of Food Technology
▶ one in the area of Textiles Technology

It does not matter if you are doing a different project from the one illustrated. You will need to think carefully about how well the check-list statement and illustration matches the level of work you are doing at present. Then look at the examples from the other areas to see if they help confirm the match. How well does your project work provide similar evidence for what is asked for in the statements on the left of the page?

Turn the page and look at the next level up. Does this provide a better match? Or maybe you need to go back to the next level down?

You only need to have achieved an aspect in one of the three areas.

You may find that you are working at different levels in different aspects (e.g. level 4 in AT1 'Have good ideas' and level 5 or 6 in AT2 'Work with materials'). This will help you spot your strengths and weaknesses.

You should discuss what level you think you are working at with your teacher.

5

Moving on up

Whatever levels you discover you are working at, your target needs to be to achieve the next one up. Don't expect to improve your levels in all aspects in each project you do.

Try to target some of your weaknesses to bring them up to the standard of the rest of your work.

If you are doing a project in which you are using unfamiliar materials or processes you might find that you will be working at a lower level than usual.

While you are working on a project you need to keep your target in mind to make sure you achieve it.

At the end of a project you should check with your teacher that you have achieved your target. If you have, you can tick the box, and write in the date and the name of the project. Then get your teacher to initial it for you.

You should also set the targets for your next project, which might be in a different D&T area.

During Key Stage 3 you need to try to improve by at least two levels. Even better, you should aim to improve your overall level by one during each year. So if, for example, you achieve level 4 in Designing and Making in Year 7, set yourself the target of reaching level 5 in Year 8 and level 6 in Year 9.

Most pupils should be achieving levels 5, 6 or 7 by the end of Year 9.

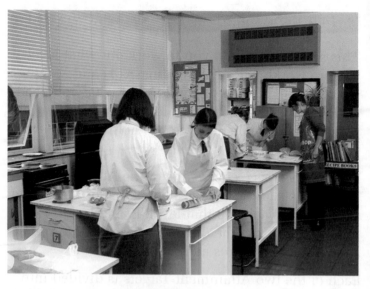

At the end of Key Stage 3

Towards the end of Year 9 your D&T teachers will need to decide what level they think you are working at. To do this they will look at a number of your projects (not just your most recent) and match them to the official National Curriculum Attainment Target statements.

They may decide that, even though you have not achieved all the aspects of a certain level in every project, you may have done enough to be awarded that level.

As well as giving you a level for AT1 and AT2 they will also work out an average level. This will be made up of 40% for AT1 and 60% for AT2. So for example if you achieved level 4 in 'Designing' and level 7 in 'Making' your final level would work out at 6.

Design and Technology at GCSE

During Year 9 you will also have to decide which area of D&T you want to study to GCSE. Your school will tell you which specialist options (e.g. Graphic Products, Food Technology) are available. Your teachers will help advise you which you would be most suited for.

All of the courses involve doing more practical coursework and gaining further knowledge and understanding. There is also a written examination at the end of the course.

You might find it helpful to study the following case-studies.

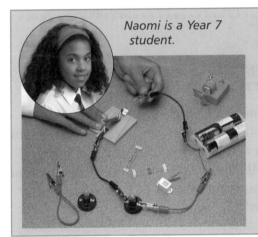

Naomi is a Year 7 student.

'The first area I worked in was Food. In my Primary School we had done some simple cooking, but when I read 'About Food Technology' I was surprised to learn what sort of things I would be doing. I remember we were set some homework tasks I didn't really understand. My parents looked at the 'D&T Dictionary' pages with me and together we were able to work out what I needed to do.

During the first term we also had lessons in making a simple electronic circuit. This was quite easy as I had done some electronics before. It wasn't long before I was able to tick several sections of the 'Materials and Components' and 'Health and Safety' pages. Looking at the levels, I seemed to be working at a mixture of levels 2 and 3, so I set myself the target of reaching level 3 in all aspects by Easter time. At the end of the year we did a short written test, and used the second section of the book to revise from.'

Simon is a Year 8 student. His previous project was to design and make a bicycle light.

'By the end of the project I had achieved all the level 4 statements in Designing and in Making. My teacher said I had also reached level 5 in 'Investigation', 'Have good ideas' and 'Evaluate', and in 'Plan the making'. Meanwhile he thought my 'Evaluate my final product' had gone really well and was already of level 6 standard.

My next project was to be in the Food Technology area. In discussion with my teacher, I agreed that I needed to pay particular attention to 'Develop my design' and 'Work with materials' to make sure I would achieve them at level 5. She suggested that in the final Year 8 Systems and Control project I could then focus on the two 'Apply what I know' level 5 statements. If all went well I would then be able to say I had achieved level 5 by the end of the Year, and was working towards level 6.

I studied the level 5 statements closely, comparing them to the level 4 ones, so that I clearly understood what I needed to do. I also looked at the level 6 statements and decided I should be able to achieve level 6 in 'Evaluate' in my next project without too much difficulty.

As I worked through my year 8 projects I covered a lot more of the areas in the 'Knowledge and Understanding' section, and was pleased to find that I only had a few boxes which had not yet been ticked.'

Magenta is a Year 9 student. She is very good at planning and making things, but finds designing much more difficult.

'At the end of Year 8 I had achieved level 6 in 'Making', but only level 4 in 'Designing'. My main target for Year 9 was therefore to see if I could progress to level 6 in Designing, My teachers were also trying to encourage me to see if I could reach a level 7 in Making. My first project was to design and make a wall-hanging in Textiles. I studied the level 5 statements and illustrations and with the help of the teacher worked out what I would have to do to reach these levels. I made sure I did some research outside school and made it clear how I had applied it when having ideas and developing my design.

I wasn't able to achieve my main target all in one go – some of the statements I had to leave until later projects. After Easter we did a final End of Key Stage Assessment Project. This was my last chance to reach level 6 in Designing, and I just managed it! I was pleased that I also managed to achieve level 7 in Making. I also did well in the final written test.

My teacher advised me to do Textiles Technology for my GCSE course, which was good because I really like working with fabrics. I wonder if I can get an A grade?'

What is Design and Technology?

We usually think of technology as being all about microchips, laser beams and fibre-optics. But technology can be simple and straightforward as well as very complex. A pencil and piece of paper are examples of technology. They enable us to record our thoughts and ideas to refer to later. With a rope we can swing across a river. Using a mirror we can flash a message to someone far away. These examples illustrate that technology exists to extend the capabilities of our minds and bodies.

Meanwhile design is the process of using technology to provide the things which people need to survive more effectively and comfortably. This involves identifying what sort of products and systems are needed, developing and proposing possible solutions to solve complex problems, communicating ideas to others, and making them happen.

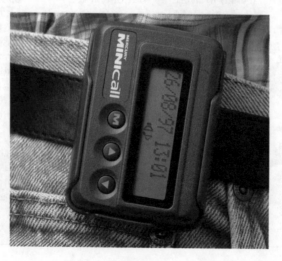

Why is Design and Technology a National Curriculum Subject?

A lot of people earn a living in one of the many areas of design and technology. This is not the main reason why you are studying the subject, however. Many of the skills you learn will be useful whatever you do when you leave school or college and enter the world of work. For example you will learn how to:

► find out about and understand the wide range of things that have to be considered when solving complicated problems
► deal with changing situations and circumstances
► experiment with new ideas and possibilities and predict how successful they are likely to be
► record your ideas and communicate them to other people more effectively
► plan and organise your time to get things done efficiently and flexibly
► evaluate how well existing products and systems have been designed so you can choose and use the best and most appropriate.

You will also get to know about how a wide range of materials behave and the tools and manufacturing processes that can be used with them. There are also plenty of opportunities to learn about the effective use of new information and communication technologies to solve problems and present your design ideas.

Design and Technology is about changing the way things are done, and the way we live our lives. Advances in technology bring benefits for some people, but hardship for others. We need to think carefully about the changes we want to make and the changes being proposed by others.

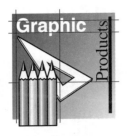

About Graphic Products

Graphic Products are the things which enable us to communicate and receive information about things like:

▷ *what's going on in the world*
▷ *how to do and use things*
▷ *how to find our way around.*

What are Graphic Products?

Books, newspapers and magazines, advertisements, CD inlays, calendars, sales brochures, tickets, stamps, bank-notes, packaging, and shop and road-signs are just a few examples of graphic products.

The majority of graphic products are two-dimensional ('flat') and are made from paper or card which has been printed on. Sometimes however the flat surface is cut and folded up into a three-dimensional shape (e.g. a 'pop-up' card or book).

The information on a TV or computer screen could also be described as a graphic product.

Designing and Making Graphic Products

To design and make graphic products in your Design and Technology lessons you will need to learn more about:

► choosing colours and creating textures
► different ways of drawing things
► selecting different styles and sizes of lettering
► arranging words and images together on a page
► the properties and characteristics of different papers, cards, pens, pencils and inks
► how things are printed or reproduced.

In your lessons you can expect to do projects in which you might be asked to design and make things like:

► pop-up cards
► instruction leaflets
► packages
► business stationery
► brochures
► symbols and logos.

Design IT!: There are many opportunities to use computers when designing graphic products. Find out what desk-top publishing, drawing and animation programs are available in your school.

9

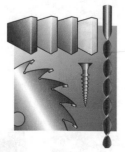

About Resistant Materials Technology

Wood, metal, plastics, ceramics and glass are all examples of resistant materials. They are used to make many of the three-dimensional products we use everyday – from teapots to trains and necklaces to knives.

We often take everyday things for granted, but someone somewhere has spent a great deal of time and effort working out:

▶ what size, shape and colour it should be
▶ what it will do
▶ how it will do it
▶ how to make it safe to use and
▶ how it is going to be made.

Products which are well designed not only work well and look good but also give the user a sense of pleasure and satisfaction.

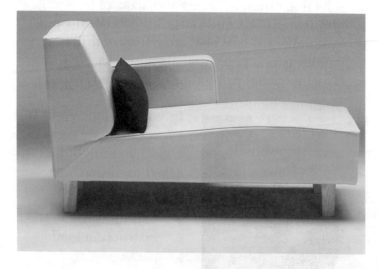

Design IT!: In industry most product design is now done on computer using 3-D modelling and drawing programs. The electronic data is then used to control manufacturing tools. Find out what facilities there are for CAD and CAD-CAM (computer-aided design and manufacture) in your school.

Designing and Making in Resistant Materials Technology

To design and make products using resistant materials you will need to learn more about:

▶ various ways of sketching, drawing and making mock-ups of things, so that you can see the design as it develops and explain your ideas to others
▶ the working properties and characteristics of a range of materials, so you can choose the ones that will be best for your design
▶ the tools and manufacturing processes used to prepare, cut, shape, form, assemble and finish different materials
▶ how to study existing products to find out more about how and why they were designed and made.

During your lessons you can expect to be asked to do projects in which you are asked to design and make things like:

▶ wooden toys
▶ jewellery
▶ containers
▶ games and puzzles.

About Systems and Electronic Products

Systems are a series of products or events which are connected in some way. Changing one part of the system affects the other parts. Structures, mechanisms and electronic circuits are all examples of systems.

Electronic products are more than just transistors and flashing LEDs. We need to be able to control what they can do, and protect their delicate components from damage.

Systems

There are lots of different sorts of systems. We are familiar with the idea of things like transport systems, biological systems and the solar system. Systems are made up of a series of sub-systems – smaller inter-connected systems.

Systems are said to have inputs, processes and outputs. The inputs are used to make the system and the outputs are the results of the system. The processes are the means by which the inputs are changed into outputs.

Systems can be controlled using switches of different types. Information (obtained from sensors) about how well the system is working is used to keep the system stable. This is known as feedback.

Electronic Products

Designing electronic products is a complex task. As well as creating a circuit that works, something is needed to keep the electronics safe from water, dust, etc. Deciding on the right type and position of displays and controls is also essential to ensure the product is easy to use. In Design and Technology you will be mainly concerned with mechanical and electronic systems – levers, pulleys, gears, components and structures which work together to make something happen.

Designing and Making Systems and Electronic Products

During your lessons you can expect to be asked to do projects in which you are asked to design and make things like:

▶ a bridge
▶ a moving vehicle
▶ a fuse tester
▶ a personal alarm
▶ a moisture sensor
▶ a night-light.

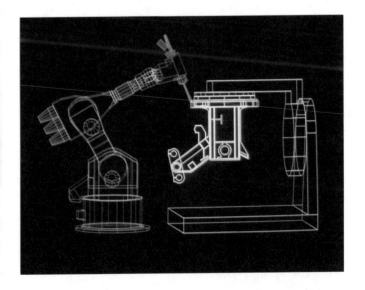

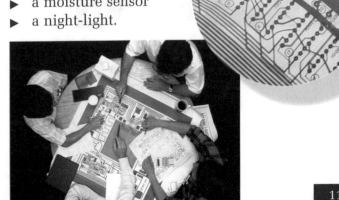

About Food Technology

Until quite recently most of the food people ate had to be produced locally. Many items were only available at certain times of the year, and didn't keep fresh for very long.

Today, however, we can buy produce from around the world, all year round. Thanks to packaging, preservatives and refrigeration we can now keep it for months.

What is Food Technology?

Food technology involves a lot more than being able to cook and knowing about nutritional requirements. In industry, food technologists need to be able to:

▶ find out exactly what sort of food products people want
▶ discover where and when they want to buy, prepare and eat them
▶ ensure the food products will be safe to eat
▶ work out how they can be produced and sold at a price people will be willing to pay
▶ calculate how many to make over what period of time.

Design IT!: *There are opportunities to use computers when designing food products. Find out what word-processing, database and spreadsheet programs are available in your school.*

Designing and Making Food Products

To design and make food products in your Design and Technology lessons you will need to learn more about:

▶ different food materials such as cereals, fruits, vegetables, eggs, meat and poultry, etc.
▶ different food products, such as biscuits, bread, soups and sauces, and using and adapting recipes
▶ preparing, combining and forming ingredients
▶ the physical, chemical and aesthetic properties of food materials and products
▶ evaluating food products using special tests.

In your lessons you can expect to do projects in which you might be asked to design and make things like:

▶ shaped biscuits
▶ new bread products
▶ pasta dishes
▶ healthy snacks
▶ vegetarian meals
▶ foods for special occasions
▶ low-fat dishes.

About Textiles Technology

From clothes to curtains and carpets to cushions, textiles is one of the world's major industries. There are countless colours, textures and patterns to choose from which can be made in an extraordinary range of fabrics each with their own individual properties and characteristics.

What is Textiles Technology?

Textiles and clothing production includes fabric design, fashion design, theatre and interior design. It's not just about choosing colours, textures and patterns that work well together, however. Textile designers also need to consider things like:

- how to add colour to fabrics in a variety of ways
- how to enrich fabrics with the application of other materials
- how different fabric blends and mixtures behave
- how textile products can be made economically in large quantities.

Designing and Making Textile Products

To design and make textile products in your Design and Technology lessons you will need to learn more about:

- different types of fibres, yarns and fabrics and their properties
- joining, cutting, shaping, combining and finishing fabrics
- creating, combining and choosing colours, patterns and textures that achieve a desired effect.

In your lessons you can expect to do projects in which you might be asked to design and make things like:

- finger puppets
- embroidered badges
- various fabric bags and containers
- T-shirts, waistcoats, hats and other items of clothing
- fabrics and fittings for specific spaces and places
- stage costumes and masks
- wall-hangings
- soft-furnishings, e.g. cushions, curtains, lampshades, etc.

Design IT!: There are plenty of opportunities to use computers when designing textile products. Find out what pattern design and layout programs and facilities for computer-aided manufacture are available in your school.

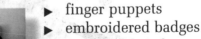

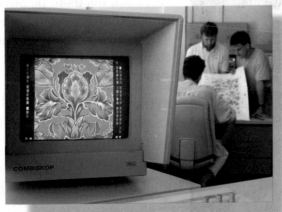

D&T Dictionary

Aesthetics

Aesthetics is all about how people respond to things through their senses. What we see, hear, taste, touch and smell can be pleasant or distressing experiences.

When designing something it is important to realise that different people like and dislike different things. Generally, however, people respond well to things that are harmonious (go together well), or provide contrast (are opposites).

Analysis

If you are asked to analyse something you will need to break it down into smaller, more detailed parts. So, for example, if you were analysing a torch you would need to describe its circuit, switch, battery, casing, etc.

Alternatively you might have been asked to analyse a problem, such as the dietary needs of a family. Again it's a matter of identifying and discussing their requirements for protein, carbohydrates, vitamins, etc.

Client

A client is the person who has asked you to design something for them. Your client could be from a large company, a local business, or simply someone you know.

Make sure you know who the users of your product will be. It will probably not be the client!

Components

Products are usually made up of a number of smaller parts, called components. Many components, such as transistors, screws, hinges, recipe ingredients and buttons are ready-made.

Conflicting Demands

Most decisions about what a design should be like involve making compromises. For example a rucksack needs to be strong but light. Generally things that are strong tend to use more material. The designer needs to choose materials and components that provide a balance between strength and weight.

Extra design features and materials that look good and last a long time are likely to increase the cost of a product.

Materials that are cheap and easy to work with might cause environmental damage.

Constraints

Constraints are things that limit the possibilities of your design. For example there may be certain sizes, weights or types of materials you cannot use, or possibly have been told you must use.

Consumers

Consumers are the people who will eventually use the products you are designing.

Remember that consumers have a choice, and if they don't want or like what you have designed, they won't use it. The particular group of consumers your product is aimed at are sometimes called the 'target market'.

As you design you must keep in mind exactly what people need physically and want emotionally. Your product needs to do the job the consumer wants it to, and make them feel good about using it.

Costs

Thinking about cost is an important part of designing. If you design something that would be expensive to make, few would be able to afford it. At the same time no-one is going to buy something which doesn't work, falls apart or looks ugly, however cheap it is.

You needn't worry too much about the exact costs when you are designing, but you do need to make sure it isn't going to be poorly made, or far too expensive.

Design Brief

The Design Brief is the starting point of a project or task. It usually contains general information about what is needed, who the product is intended for and any major constraints.

Sometimes a brief can be very specific (e.g. design a toy for a 6-year old made in wood with one moving part, based on a wild animal), or very open (e.g. design a toy for a child). Most briefs are a mixture of the two.

Dear Ms Smith

As we discussed I would like you to develop some design ideas for a new range of computer workstations, suitable for use in Design and Technology studios in schools. It is essential that they are low-cost and can be self-assembled on site.
I look forward to meeting you again after you have done some initial investigation into possible shapes, sizes, materials and design features.

Yours sincerely

Design Proposals

A design proposal is a suggestion for a possible solution which you present to someone else for their comments. Throughout a project you are likely to need to produce several design proposals for approval by your client (or in school your teacher) until you reach your final solution.

Design Specifications

A specification is a precise description of what a product or system must be like. It usually contains information about minimum and maximum sizes, weights, safety requirements, costs, appearance, materials, methods of production, etc.

As a design is being developed, the specification will become more and more detailed.

D&T Dictionary

Disassemble

This means to take something apart. In D&T work this does not necessarily mean pulling something to pieces. You can visually disassemble something just by looking at it very closely and from all angles. The purpose of disassembling an existing product or system is to learn more about how it works and how it was made, and to discuss the success of the design.

As you disassemble something, see if you can work out the designer's original brief and what the final specification might have been.

There are some examples of studies of disassembled products on pages 32, 33 and 34.

Durability

Durability means how long a product is likely to last. How much wear and tear will it take before it stops working?

As you design, remember that there's not much point proposing a component that will last for a hundred years if some other part of the design is likely to become unusable after a year or so.

Environmental Impact

Everything we make has an effect on the natural eco-system of our planet and there is a danger that the system could become permanently damaged. There is no such thing as a completely environmentally-friendly product, but it is possible to reduce the extent of the damage caused to help maintain a balance.

In your project work you should aim to produce designs that:

▶ use less materials and energy in their production
▶ can be re-cycled or re-used and easily maintained.

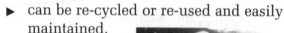

Evaluation

When you are asked to evaluate an existing product or your own design work you need to do more than just describe it. Make sure you also comment on its quality – how good or bad it is.

When evaluating a product you might find it helpful to compare it to other similar products. Does the design solve a particular problem less or more successfully than another? You could also mention what other people say about the design – their views might be different from yours. You could refer to the results of tests as evidence of how well it works.

When evaluating your own performance you will need to comment on the aspects of your work (e.g. investigating, planning, making, etc.) that have been the most successful. You will also need to say something about:

▶ what you find difficult and why
▶ if you managed to achieve the targets you set yourself
▶ which of your strengths and weakness you are planning to build on in your next project.

Flow-chart

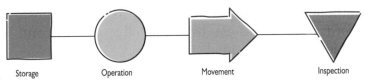

Storage   Operation   Movement   Inspection

A flow chart is a diagram of a sequence of events. It makes planning much easier and more effective.

A flow-chart can be quite simple, just showing the order in which to do a number of stages. These stages can be broken down into more detailed flow-charts showing each action in more detail.

At the other extreme a flow-chart can also show a complex pattern of procedures, indicating overlapping events, time-scales and on-going costs.

Function

The function of a product means what it is intended to do. A cup is made to hold liquids and look attractive. A watch needs to tell the time accurately and be small and light enough to wear on your wrist.

Many objects have more than one function. For example spoons can be used to eat or drink from, or to stir liquids. They can also be used to measure ingredients. Some spoons are used as commemorative souvenirs.

As you design, remember that your product might have a variety of functions.

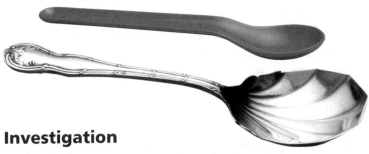

Investigation

To investigate something means to examine, inquire into, or to find out more about it.

In your Design and Technology work you will need to do some investigations to learn more about things like:

▶ the people you are designing for
▶ what they want your design to do for them
▶ how it might work
▶ what it might be made from
▶ how it might be made.

To find the answers to these sorts of questions you will need to:

▶ observe and talk to potential users
▶ consult books and other documents
▶ contact experts to ask for advice.

As you plan and undertake your research you need to keep asking if the information you are discovering is relevant to your task. As you develop your design ideas you need to make sure you are taking what you have discovered into account.

D&T Dictionary

Information Technology

Computers are changing our lives. They have also had a major impact on the way products are designed and made. There are many opportunities in Design and Technology to use computers. Find out what facilities exist in your school. Think carefully about when it is appropriate to use them.

Computer-aided design (CAD)

There are many different types of CAD packages. Some are two-dimensional and are commonly known as drawing, paint or desk-top publishing or desk-top video programs. Others are three-dimensional, allowing the screen images to be turned and looked at from different angles. Some programs make animation in two dimensions or three dimensions easy.

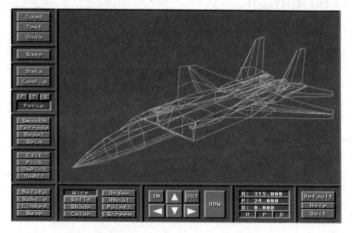

Computer-aided manufacture (CAM)

Two-dimensional computer-aided designs can be printed out or saved to a disk. Data from three dimensional designs can be sent directly to machine tools which can produce solid objects automatically.

Control systems

Computers can be used to control sequences of events, turning circuits on and off, speeding things up or slowing them down and feeding back information from sensing devices to keep things running smoothly.

Databases

Databases are organised collections of information (text and/or images) which are held or organised on a computer. A database can search, cross-reference and present information very quickly, and can be extremely useful during the investigating stages of a Design and Technology project.

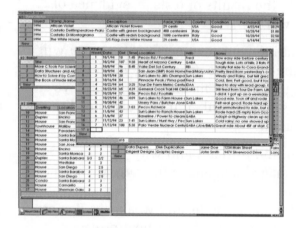

Presentation packages

These programs enable you to present information on screen. You could use one to explain to an audience the main features of your design proposal. Words and images can be animated and sound and video sequences added.

Other similar programs are called 'Multimedia Authoring Packages'. You could also use one of these to create an interactive game or entertainment.

Project management

These packages can help you plan and organise project work. They enable different types of flow-chart to be produced on screen and can quickly calculate alterations to times and costs if changes are made. Electronic organisers can provide automatic reminders of approaching deadlines and things that need to be done at once.

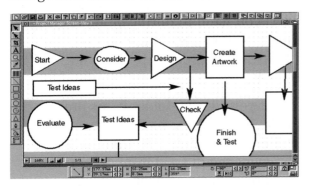

Spreadsheets

Spreadsheets help with complex calculations. Once set up they can be used to calculate the effect of changing one element of a design on all the other parts. The data from a spreadsheet can also be displayed quickly as a graph or chart.

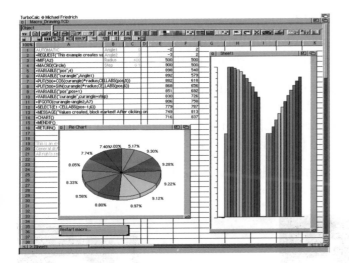

Word-processing

Word-processors are sophisticated typewriters that enable text to be checked and changed before being printed out. Word-processed text can be easily placed into desk-top publishing programs where it can be laid out in columns and placed next to illustrations.

Manufacturing

There are a number of ways in which products are made:

▶ One-off production is where a single item is made on its own.
▶ Batch production is where a specific number of items are made together, saving time and materials. The production line can then be changed quickly to make a batch of a different design.
▶ Mass-production is where identical products are made all the time. The different stages are usually carried out by different people, working on a conveyor-belt system.

Templates

These are useful in batch and mass-production. These are standard shapes which can be used as a pattern for cutting identical pieces.

Jigs

Jigs are specially made tools which quickly place materials, tools and components in the right position.

Moulds

These are often used to produce identical copies of shapes and forms. Pliable or liquid material is usually placed over or in a mould. As it hardens it takes on the shape of the mould. Alternatives to moulds are 'pressings' and 'castings'.

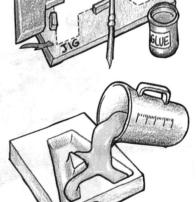

As you develop your design ideas you will need to consider how they can be made as a one-off item in school and in quantity.

D&T Dictionary

Models and Modelling

A 'model' of a new design is often made to show a client or potential consumer before it is produced in quantity.

However the idea of 'modelling' is slightly different. Making new products take a lot of time, effort and money, so it's a good idea to try your designs out as much possible so that mistakes can be avoided.

To discover if something will work you don't have to make it the same size as the real thing, or using the same materials. Drawings, diagrams, mock-ups, prototypes and test and trial pieces are all quicker and cheaper to create than the real thing.

In your Design and Technology work think carefully about what you want to learn about your design from your modelling and decide which is the best sort of model to make to get the information you need.

Presentation

The way you present your Design and Technology work is very important. The sequence of sheets (or Design Folder) you hand in during or at the end of a project needs to show clearly the process you have used to investigate, develop, plan and evaluate your design ideas.

Remember that your design folder helps provide important evidence that you have achieved your targets. Good presentation won't cover up poor thinking, but evidence of good thinking can easily get lost if the presentation is poor.

You also need to present your final design proposal. This will be separate from your design folder. It needs to show what your idea is rather than how you got there. This presentation might involve explanatory drawings, samples, photographs, three-dimensional models, etc.

Products

Products are the things which are made (or 'produced') as the result of designing.

Products can be two-dimensional (e.g. Graphic Products), three-dimensional (e.g. Resistant Materials and Electronics), wearable (e.g. Textiles), or edible (e.g. Food).

Buildings and the spaces and places in and around them are also products.

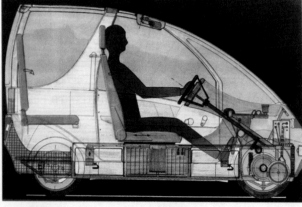

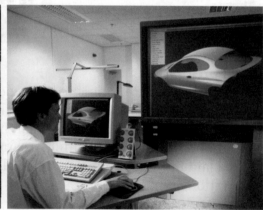

Properties and Characteristics of Materials

Different materials behave in different ways. They are said to have different physical and chemical properties. For example a piece of plastic bends and melts when heated, whilst a piece of fabric burns. When some materials are processed or combined in a particular way their behaviour can change.

Materials with similar properties and characteristics can be grouped together for easy reference.

Knowing how different materials can be shaped, formed, combined and finished is essential for a designer.

Resources

Resources are the things available to you to help you complete your project. The materials, components and tools and the space you have to work in at your school are perhaps your most obvious resources.

Another important and precious resource is that of time. Use it wisely, and don't waste it! Your own skills are a resource too: you may have to learn or practise some specific skills for a particular task.

Books and other sources of information are resources. 'Experts' are another resource. Ask your teacher for help and advice if there is something you are not sure about. Sometimes you may need to go and consult other people for more specialist knowledge.

Sketches

A sketch is a particular type of drawing used to record information and explore ideas. Sketches should not be drawn very neatly using a ruler: this takes too long – they need to be quick so you can move on rapidly. Sketches often include notes or labels to help explain the ideas or to record passing thoughts. Sometimes they include colour, particularly if it is an important part of the design.

Survey

A survey is an investigation of things people do and/or what they think and feel about certain things. Such information helps to identify the products they are most likely to need and want.

There are a number of ways this information might be gathered. One is to interview a small number of people individually, or hold a discussion group session (known as a 'focus' group). Another is to use a questionnaire. This enables a larger number of people to be surveyed. Questionnaires need to be carefully planned and tested if they are to produce information which is helpful and reliable.

Workshop Drawings

Unlike sketches, workshop drawings need to be very neat and accurate. They need to show exact sizes and shapes of all the materials and components needed to make the design. It should be possible for someone else to make up the design from your drawings. Workshop drawings are usually laid out in orthographic projection, that is a plan and two elevations, with each part numbered and described in a table on the drawing.

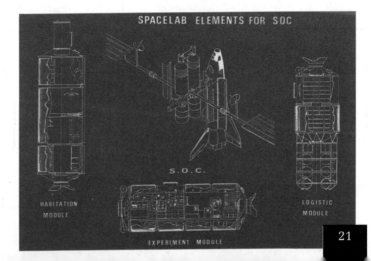

Materials and Components

You will need to choose materials and components that have the most suitable properties and characteristics for your design.

Different materials have:
- ❏ different physical properties and
- ❏ different chemical properties.

Materials can be grouped together into certain types which have similar properties and characteristics.

The properties and characteristics of materials can be changed by:
- ❏ combining
- ❏ processing
- ❏ finishing.

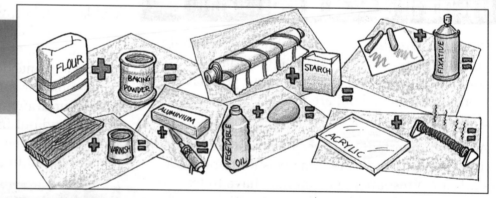

Some materials can be formed by
- ❏ pressing
- ❏ casting
- ❏ moulding.

This is important when making multiple copies.

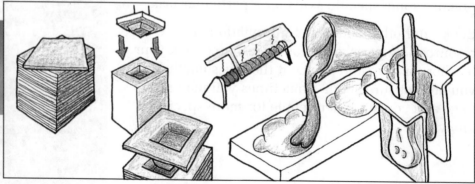

Graphic Products

Materials and Components

Paper and boards:
- ❏ sizes
- ❏ weights
- ❏ colours
- ❏ finishes.

Pens and pencils:
- ❏ graphite
- ❏ coloured
- ❏ felt-markers
- ❏ chalks and pastels.

Paints and inks:
- ❏ water-based
- ❏ PVA-based.

Printing methods:
- ❏ block printing
- ❏ screenprinting
- ❏ laser printing
- ❏ photocopying
- ❏ photography.

Typography:
- ❏ sizes and styles of lettering
- ❏ letter and line spacing.

Drawing systems:
- ❏ graphs, charts and diagrams
- ❏ plans and elevations
- ❏ orthographics
- ❏ isometrics
- ❏ dimensioning
- ❏ cut-aways
- ❏ exploded and perspective drawings.

Resistant Materials Technology

Materials and Components

Wood

There are two main types of wood:

- ❏ hardwoods come from deciduous trees, e.g. oak, beech
- ❏ softwoods come from coniferous trees, e.g. spruce, pine.

Manufactured boards

- ❏ Manufactured boards are made from either wood particles or veneers glued together, heated and compressed, e.g. plywood, MDF, chipboard.

Metals

- ❏ Pure metals, e.g. copper, aluminium, silver.
- ❏ Metal alloys, e.g. brass (copper and zinc), steel (iron and carbon).

Plastics

There are two types of plastics:

- ❏ thermosets, e.g. polyester resin, melanine formaldeyde.
- ❏ thermoplastics, e.g. acrylics, polythene, PVC.

Glass, concrete and ceramics are also resistant materials.

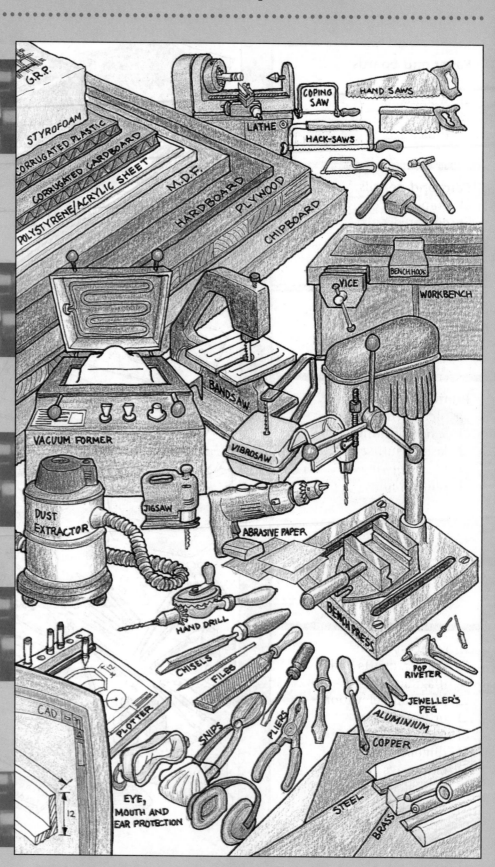

Electronic Products/ Systems and Control

Materials and Components

- ❑ Electricity and electrical circuits
- ❑ Voltage, current and resistance

- ❑ Batteries and power supplies
- ❑ Wires
- ❑ Switches
- ❑ Resistors
- ❑ Diodes
- ❑ Capacitors
- ❑ Transistors
- ❑ Sensors
- ❑ Timers
- ❑ Integrated circuits

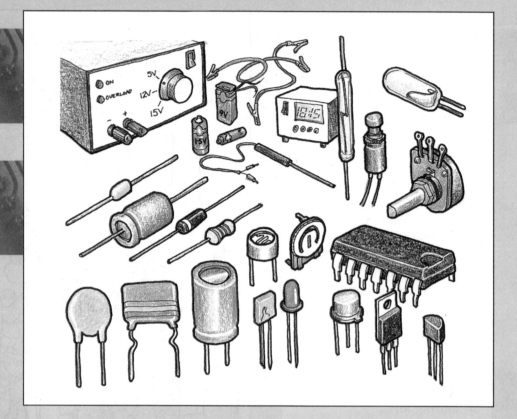

- ❑ Input devices
- ❑ Output devices
- ❑ Interfaces
- ❑ Control languages
- ❑ Timing events
- ❑ Analogue devices
- ❑ Closed loop systems

- ❑ Pneumatic systems
- ❑ Using syringes
- ❑ Compressors
- ❑ Valves and cylinders
- ❑ Simple circuits

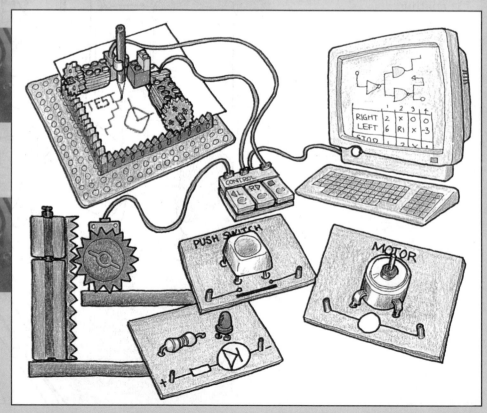

Food Technology

Materials and Components

There are many types of basic food materials:

- ❏ cereals
- ❏ dairy products
- ❏ eggs
- ❏ fats/oils
- ❏ fish
- ❏ fruits
- ❏ meat/poultry
- ❏ nuts
- ❏ pulses
- ❏ Quorn /Tofu
- ❏ sugars
- ❏ vegetables.

Many food products involve mixing different ingredients together.

Properties of food materials can be changed by:

- ❏ adding air
- ❏ coating
- ❏ encasing
- ❏ flavouring
- ❏ glazing
- ❏ heating
- ❏ hydrating
- ❏ shortening
- ❏ thickening.

Textiles Technology

Materials and Components

There are three types of fibres:
- ❏ natural
- ❏ synthetic
- ❏ regenerated.

Fabrics can be bonded by:
- ❏ stitching
- ❏ gluing
- ❏ heating
- ❏ steaming
- ❏ laminating
- ❏ stapling
- ❏ tying.

Designing and making with fabrics involves choosing and using processes of:
- ❏ cutting
- ❏ joining
- ❏ combining
- ❏ adding to a surface
- ❏ shaping into 3D
- ❏ finishing.

Unusual fabrics such as strips of plastic, grasses and discarded houshold items can be woven, knitted and crocheted into fabrics.

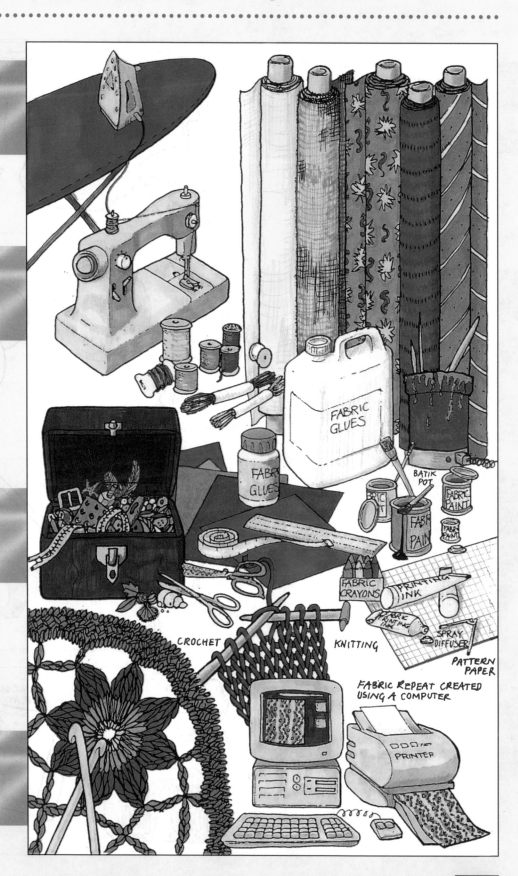

Systems and Control

Systems involve a number of things happening in a particular sequence to produce a desired outcome. They have:
- ❑ inputs
- ❑ processes
- ❑ outputs.

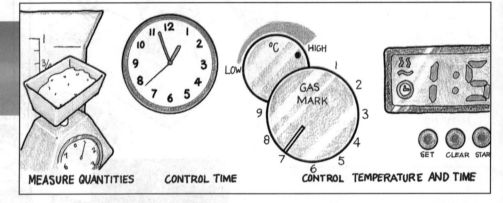

Systems need to be kept in control otherwise they would start to go wrong.

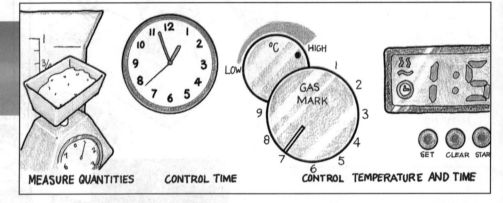

Controls enable people to pass information to a machine or device to make it work as intended.

Two methods of control are:
- ❑ sensors
- ❑ switches.

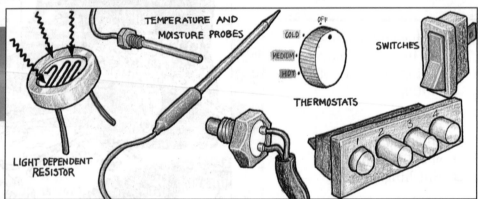

Displays are used to pass information about what is happening in a system to the user of the machine or device.

This is called feedback.

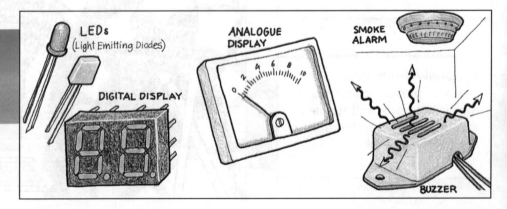

Mechanisms

Systems and Control

Wheel and axle
- ❏ Gears and cams can change the direction of movement.
- ❏ Gears can speed movement up or slow it down.
- ❏ A fixed pulley rotates on its axle. A block and tackle is made up up of several fixed and moving pulleys.

Levers
- ❏ Two or more levers joined together make a linkage.
- ❏ A linkage can change the direction and the size of a movement.
- ❏ Levers do not have to be straight.

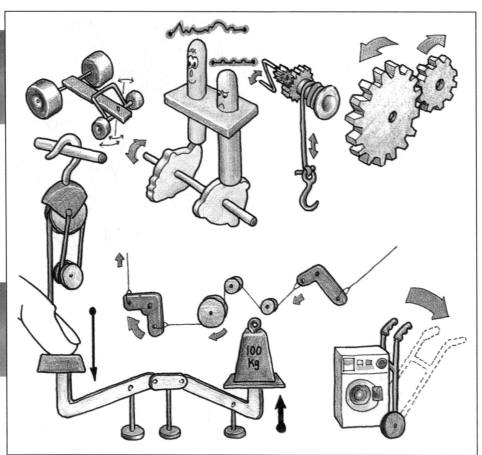

Inclined plane
- ❏ The effort needed to move an object up a slope is roughly half of that needed to move it vertically to the same height.
- ❏ A wedge is a slope which is thin at one end and thick at the other.

The screw
- ❏ The screw is a spiral thread or groove cut into a piece of cylindrical material such as wood or metal.

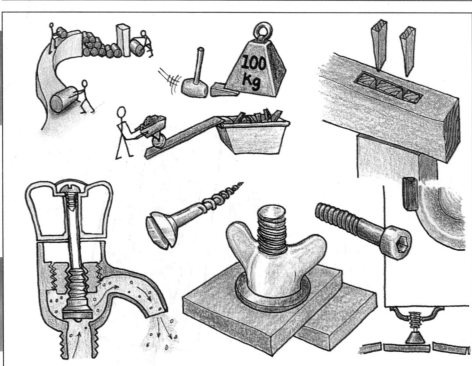

Mechanical, Pneumatic and Electronic Control

Systems and Control

Mechanical control
- ❑ Mechanisms can be interconnected to form a system which changes one kind of movement into another.
- ❑ Movement can be speeded up or slowed down.

Pneumatic control
- ❑ Air pressure is used to provide motion by moving a controlled volume of air along a tube and through valves.
- ❑ Valves control the flow of compressed air, pushing pistons up or down.
- ❑ Hydraulic systems use fluids instead of air when greater force needs to be transmitted.

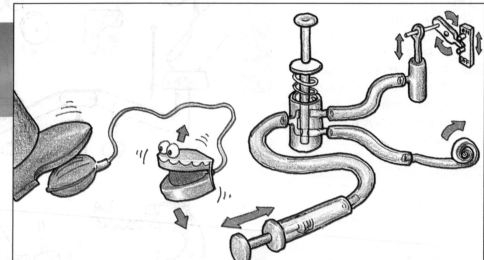

Electronic control
A system of electronic components can be used to:
- ❑ switch circuits on and off
- ❑ increase or decrease the amount of electricity flowing around a circuit
- ❑ count the number of times something happens
- ❑ delay a component from working for a set time.

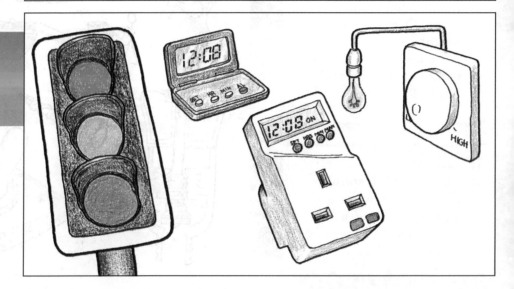

Structures

There are two main types of structure:
❏ frame structures
❏ shell structures.
Some objects combine both types of structure.

Structures can be stabilised by:
❏ a low centre of gravity or a wide base
❏ triangulation
❏ bending and folding
❏ adding ribs.

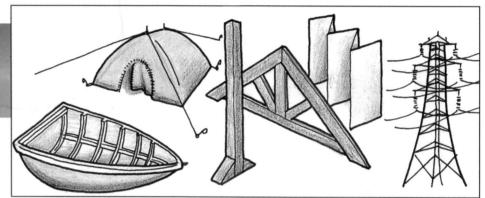

There are two types of force:
❏ dynamic (moving) forces which produce movement
❏ static (still) forces which cancel each other out.

The main forces that act upon structures are:
❏ tension (stretching)
❏ compression (pushing)
❏ torsion (twisting)
❏ bending
❏ shearing (cutting).

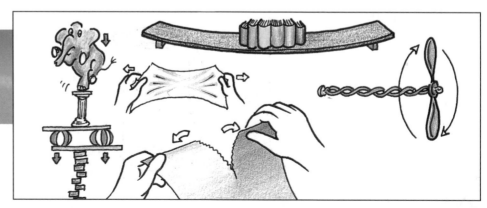

Product Design

Products and Applications/Quality

When studying an existing product you need to:
- ❑ say what it is for
- ❑ discover how it works
- ❑ find out what materials and components have been used
- ❑ explain why the designer has chosen those particular materials and components
- ❑ suggest what tools and processes have been used to make it.

You also need to compare the product with other similar designs:
- ❑ which do you think have the best features?
- ❑ which do other users prefer?

As well as describing your product you need to say how well it has been designed and made in terms of its:
- ❑ purpose (how well does it meet a clear need?)
- ❑ materials (could better or less materials have been used?)
- ❑ durability (how well made is it?)
- ❑ ease of repair
- ❑ environmental impact (can it be re-used or re-cycled?)
- ❑ social, moral and cultural issues (does it have any undesired side-effects on people?).

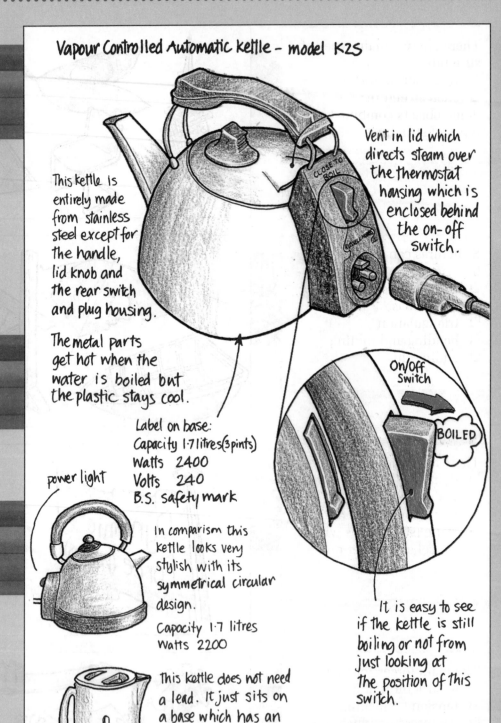

Vapour Controlled Automatic Kettle – model K25

This kettle is entirely made from stainless steel except for the handle, lid knob and the rear switch and plug housing.

The metal parts get hot when the water is boiled but the plastic stays cool.

Vent in lid which directs steam over the thermostat housing which is enclosed behind the on-off switch.

On/Off Switch

BOILED

Label on base:
Capacity 1·7 litres (3 pints)
Watts 2400
Volts 240
B.S. safety mark

power light

In comparism this kettle looks very stylish with its symmetrical circular design.
Capacity 1·7 litres
Watts 2200

This kettle does not need a lead. It just sits on a base which has an integral power connector.

Capacity 2 litres
Watts 2200

water level indicator

It is easy to see if the kettle is still boiling or not from just looking at the position of this switch.

Kettle features:
Descaling filters
Safety cut-outs
Quick boiling
Well balanced

Food Technology

Products and Applications/Quality

When studying an existing food product you need to:
- ❏ say who might buy and eat it and when
- ❏ list the ingredients it contains and say how it should be stored / heated / served
- ❏ explain why the main ingredients have been chosen
- ❏ suggest how it has been made and the equipment and processes used to make it.

You also need to compare your product with other similar designs:
- ❏ which do you think is the most appealing, and why?
- ❏ what do other people think?

As well as describing your product you need to say how well it has been designed and made in terms of its:
- ❏ purpose (how well does it meet a clear need?)
- ❏ ingredients (could better or more or less materials have been used?)
- ❏ nutritional value (is it a healthy product?)
- ❏ ease of preparation and serving
- ❏ environmental impact (can the packaging be re-used or re-cycled?)
- ❏ reflection of the social, moral and cultural needs of those it is intended for.

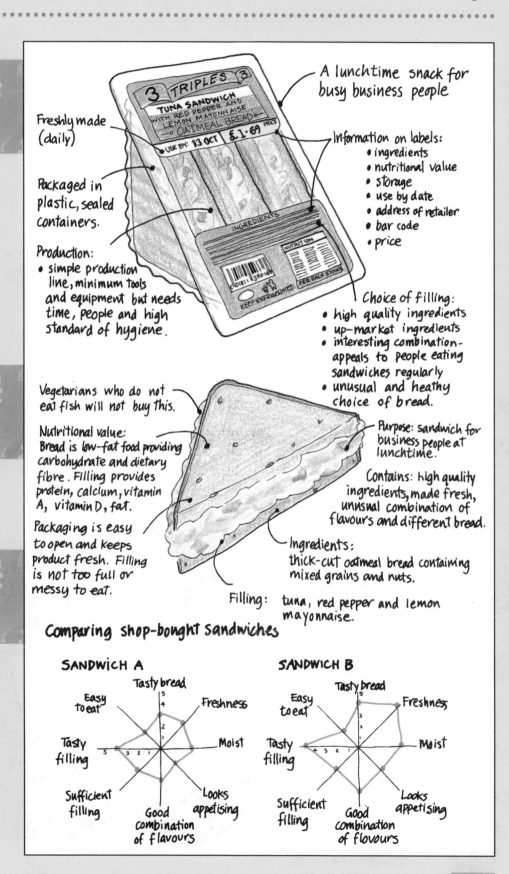

A lunchtime snack for busy business people

Freshly made (daily)

Packaged in plastic, sealed containers.

Production:
- simple production line, minimum tools and equipment but needs time, people and high standard of hygiene.

Information on labels:
- ingredients
- nutritional value
- storage
- use by date
- address of retailer
- bar code
- price

Choice of filling:
- high quality ingredients
- up-market ingredients
- interesting combination - appeals to people eating sandwiches regularly
- unusual and heathy choice of bread.

Vegetarians who do not eat fish will not buy this.

Nutritional value:
Bread is low-fat food providing carbohydrate and dietary fibre. Filling provides protein, calcium, vitamin A, vitamin D, fat.

Packaging is easy to open and keeps product fresh. Filling is not too full or messy to eat.

Purpose: sandwich for business people at lunchtime.

Contains: high quality ingredients, made fresh, unusual combination of flavours and different bread.

Ingredients:
thick-cut oatmeal bread containing mixed grains and nuts.

Filling: tuna, red pepper and lemon mayonnaise.

Comparing shop-bought sandwiches

SANDWICH A

SANDWICH B

Textiles Technology

Products and Applications/Quality

When studying an existing textile product you need to:

❑ say what it is for
❑ discover how it has been put together
❑ find out what fabrics have been used
❑ explain why the designer has chosen those fabrics, e.g. for strength, surface finish, decoration, etc?
❑ suggest what techniques have been used to make it, e.g. applique, weaving, etc.

You also need to compare the product with other similar textile designs:

❑ which do you think have the most successful features?
❑ which do other people prefer?

As well as describing the product you need to say how well it has been designed and made in terms of its:

❑ fitness for purpose
❑ fabrics and decorative elements
❑ durability (how well made is it?)
❑ environmental impact (can the fabrics and components be re-used or re-cycled?)
❑ reflection of the social, moral and cultural needs of those it is intended for?

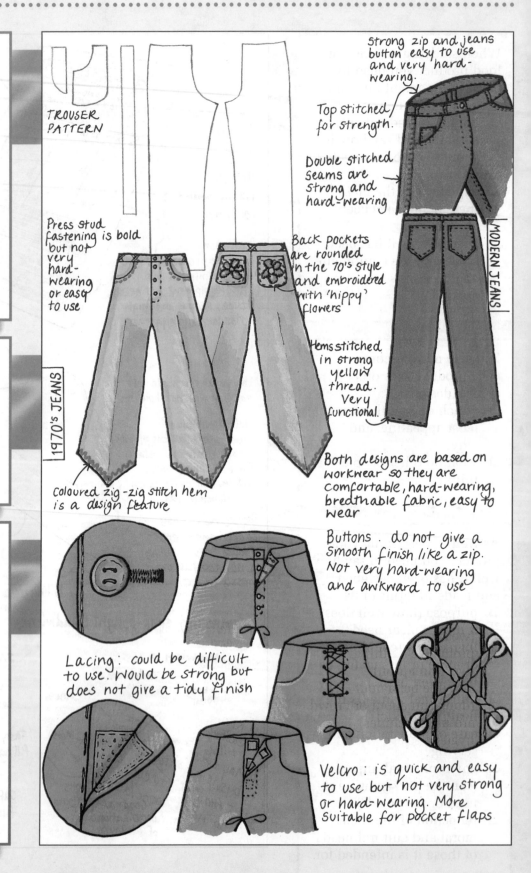

TROUSER PATTERN

strong zip and jeans button easy to use and very hard-wearing.

Top stitched for strength.

Double stitched seams are strong and hard-wearing

Press stud fastening is bold but not very hard-wearing or easy to use

Back pockets are rounded in the 70's style and embroidered with 'hippy' flowers

Hems stitched in strong yellow thread. Very functional.

1970's JEANS

MODERN JEANS

Coloured zig-zig stitch hem is a design feature

Both designs are based on workwear so they are comfortable, hard-wearing, breathable fabric, easy to wear

Buttons. do not give a smooth finish like a zip. Not very hard-wearing and awkward to use

Lacing: could be difficult to use. Would be strong but does not give a tidy finish

Velcro: is quick and easy to use but not very strong or hard-wearing. More suitable for pocket flaps

34

Health and Safety

As a designer you must think about the potential hazards for people who will use your product.

What are the risks that they might harm themselves from things like:
- ❏ sharp edges
- ❏ electrical circuits
- ❏ contaminated food.

You also need to consider the possible dangers in making your designs.
- ❏ Make sure you keep risks to a minimum by following safety rules and regulations at all times. Study warning notices and posters carefully.

It is your responsibility to check the following:
- ❏ electrical safety (always ask permission before using electric tools)
- ❏ hot or sharp tools (handle with care)
- ❏ fumes and dust (wear a mask)
- ❏ eye protection (wear goggles)
- ❏ protective clothing (wear an apron)
- ❏ sensible behaviour (don't run about or crowd around machines)
- ❏ hygiene (wash your hands when working with food)
- ❏ food storage conditions
- ❏ clean and tidy work areas.

Designing: Levels 1 and 2

To achieve Levels 1 and 2 I will need to:

Investigate

- ❑ Find out some information that will help me to develop my design.
- ❑ Try out my ideas using some materials.

Date: Project: Teacher:

Have good ideas

- ❑ Experiment by cutting, shaping and joining the materials in different ways.

Date: Project: Teacher:

Develop my design

- ❑ Show my ideas on paper using words and pictures.
- ❑ Test my ideas and make 3D models of them.

Date: Project: Teacher:

Apply what I know

- ❑ Say where I think my ideas came from, e.g.: how other things I have seen before work, what they are made from and how they are made.

Date: Project: Teacher:

Evaluate

- ❑ Say which I think are my best ideas. Why?
- ❑ Look closely at some familiar products and say how well I think they work.
- ❑ Think carefully about how good my ideas are.
- ❑ Talk to someone else about my ideas, and say how they might be improved.

Date: Project: Teacher:

Product Design

MY PROJECT WAS TO DESIGN AND MAKE A PULL-ALONG TOY FOR A YOUNG CHILD

Food Technology

MY PROJECT WAS TO DESIGN AND MAKE SOME ANIMAL BISCUITS TO EAT WITH FRIENDS AT BREAK-TIME

Textiles Technology

MY PROJECT WAS TO DESIGN AND MAKE FINGER-PUPPETS BASED ON A FAIRY TALE

WHICH ANIMAL SHAPES COULD I USE?

shapes

Best Recipes

WHICH STORY SHOULD I CHOOSE?

I DID SOME EXPERIMENTS

HOW LARGE DO THE PUPPETS NEED TO BE?

I measured the distance from the end of my finger to my knuckle to work out the size of my puppets.

FELT

HESSIAN

I MADE UP THE RECIPE

50g caster sugar ✓
100g butter ✓
150g plain flour ✓
Gas mark 4, 10-15 mins. ✓

I TESTED SOME METHODS OF JOINING THE MATERIALS

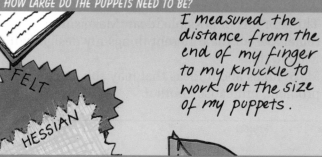

I cut out some fabrics to the right size.

COTTON

I tried to join the pieces with glue, staples and stitching.

WHICH INGREDIENTS WOULD BE BEST?

My whale biscuit would look better if the face had an eye.

I could use:
- sultanas/raisins
- chocolate chips
- smarties

WHAT ARE OTHER FINGER PUPPETS LIKE?

I went to a toy shop to see what sort of puppets they had and how they were made. This gave me some design ideas.

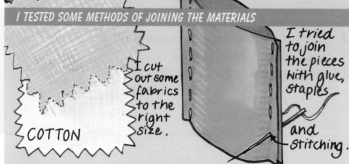

Head and body are cut from one piece of felt. The nose is embroidered and the whiskers are made of thread.

I DISCUSSED MY IDEAS WITH MY TEACHER

The size and shape of my biscuits will be just right because I will use a cutter.

cutting edge

HOW COULD I IMPROVE MY DESIGN?

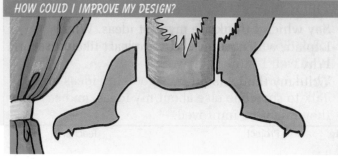

Designing: Level 3

To achieve Level 3 I will need to:

Product Design

MY PROJECT WAS TO DESIGN AND MAKE AN ENAMELLED BADGE BASED ON AN ANIMAL SHAPE

Investigate

❑ Make a list of all the things my final design has got to be able to do, based on what I have found out.
❑ Say which features are the most important.
❑ Explain which things might make others difficult to do.

Date: Project: Teacher:

Have good ideas

❑ Think of lots of possible ideas. Make sure I remember all the different things my design will need to do.
❑ Make notes about ideas that may solve one problem, but cause another.

Date: Project: Teacher:

Develop my design

❑ Show the most important parts of my design using labelled sketches.
❑ Suggest some other ideas to my teacher.

Date: Project: Teacher:

Apply what I know

❑ Develop and improve my ideas by using what I have recently learnt about different materials, components and ways of doing things.

Date: Project: Teacher:

Evaluate

❑ Say which I think are my best ideas. Why?
❑ Explain which of my ideas are least likely to work. Why?
❑ Write my thoughts down.

Date: Project: Teacher:

WHAT HAD MY DESIGN GOT TO BE ABLE TO DO?

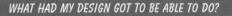

My brooch must
• be safe
• look like my chosen animal
• be as light as ...

Enamel and copper are heavy but my badge must be light.

I NEEDED SOME DIFFERENT IDEAS

① ② ③

It must look like a cat but also be a simple shape to cut out.

THE METHOD OF FIXING WAS IMPORTANT

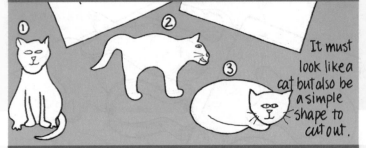

Enamel lumps

BACK   Brooch Pin

FRONT
Black enamel   copper wire

MY TEACHER HAD SHOWN US HOW TO ENAMEL

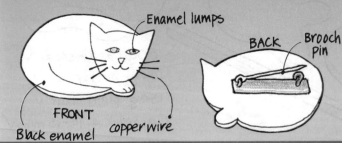

Successful Enamelling

Kiln

HOW COULD I IMPROVE MY IDEAS?

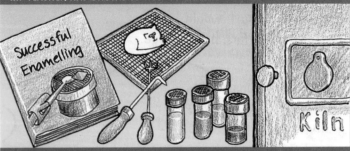

I liked my first idea best, but it was too complicated to cut out. I chose the third idea, but the whiskers will be hard to do.

Food Technology

MY PROJECT WAS TO DESIGN AND MAKE A RANGE OF LOW-COST HEALTHY MEALS USING FRUIT

Textiles Technology

MY PROJECT WAS TO DESIGN AND MAKE A BAG TO CARRY ART MATERIALS. IT HAD TO USE NATURAL FIBRES AND HAVE AN AFRICAN THEME

I NEEDED TO FIND OUT MORE ABOUT DIFFERENT TYPES OF FRUIT

In order of importance my designs must:
- include fruit
- be low in fat, sugar
- ... salt
- ... fibre
- be high ...
- be economical

Some fruits are expensive – which cost less?

HOW CAN I USE FRUIT THAT ARE CHEAP, BUT NOT HIGH IN FIBRE

Fruits
- bananas
- Kiwis
- pears
- grapes
- mangoes
- peaches
- oranges
- pomegranates

IDEAS
fruit trifle
chicken curry and apricot
sausage and apple casserole
tropical rice salad

WHICH ARE THE MOST IMPORTANT INGREDIENTS?

- sultanas
- mango
- long grain rice
- peanuts
- cherries
- pineapple

- add paw-paw?
- use wild rice?

I IMPROVED MY IDEA BY REDUCING ITS COST

Fresh pineapple is expensive...

...Could I use tinned pineapple instead?

WHICH OF MY IDEAS WERE BEST, AND WHY?

My best idea is the rice salad. It will be easy and economical. The range of fruit will be unusual and contrast well with the wild rice.

trifle
chicken curry
apricot
IDEAS

THERE WERE MANY QUESTIONS I NEEDED TO ANSWER

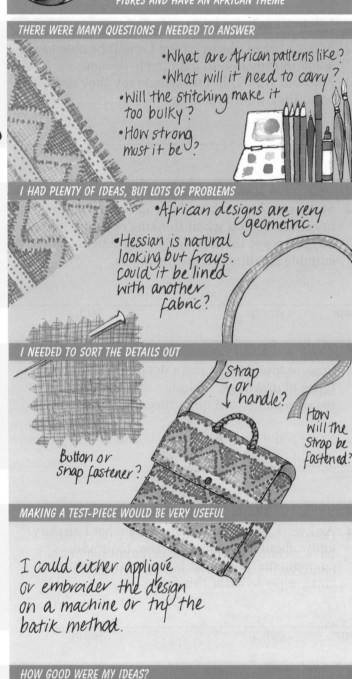

- What are African patterns like?
- What will it need to carry?
- Will the stitching make it too bulky?
- How strong must it be?

I HAD PLENTY OF IDEAS, BUT LOTS OF PROBLEMS

- African designs are very geometric.
- Hessian is natural looking but frays. Could it be lined with another fabric?

I NEEDED TO SORT THE DETAILS OUT

Button or snap fastener?

strap or handle?

How will the strap be fastened?

MAKING A TEST-PIECE WOULD BE VERY USEFUL

I could either appliqué or embroider the design on a machine or try the batik method.

HOW GOOD WERE MY IDEAS?

Shoulder strap is easier to carry things with.

Hessian won't take wax resist well. I need to use appliqué.

Lined hessian is strong and not too heavy.

Designing: Level 4

To achieve Level 4 I will need to:

MY PROJECT WAS TO DESIGN AND MAKE A 'POP-UP' GREETINGS CARD

Investigate

❑ Make a list of places where I might be able to get some information to help me to design.

❑ Find out what different people say they need, and what they would like.

Date: Project: Teacher:

I NEEDED TO PLAN MY INVESTIGATION

Where can I go?
- Greetings card and book shops
- Ask family and friends
- Study my own collection of pop-up books

What sort of birthday cards do you buy?
What sort do you like to receive?

Have good ideas

❑ Make sure I use what I have found out through my investigation when thinking of design ideas.

❑ Suggest ways that my design could be made suitable for different people to use.

Date: Project: Teacher:

WHAT THEME COULD I USE?

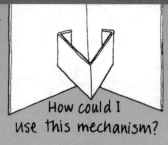

The theme of fireworks seems popular.

How could I use this mechanism?

Develop my design

❑ Present my ideas in more detail using different types of drawings. Include some colour. Add measurements and quantities. Remember to use labels.

❑ Make some simple 3D models and/or test-pieces to try out my ideas.

Date: Project: Teacher:

I TRIED OUT SOME IDEAS IN CARD

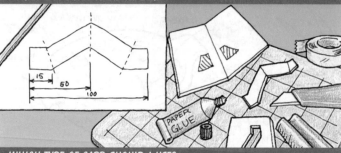

15   60   100

PAPER GLUE

Apply what I know

❑ As I work, make sure I am using what I already know about different materials, tools and components, and what I have recently learnt in class, especially for this task.

Date: Project: Teacher:

WHICH TYPE OF CARD SHOULD I USE?

score folds

I tried different thicknesses of card and fixing methods on my models to see which worked best.

I used what I knew about how to cut and fold card accurately.

Evaluate

❑ Keep looking back at my work to make sure my ideas are solving the original problem.

❑ Keep checking that my designs will be suitable for use by different people.

Date: Project: Teacher:

AM I SOLVING THE PROBLEM?

Fireworks are liked by boys, girls and adults.

HAPPY BIRTHDAY

Food Technology

MY PROJECT WAS TO DESIGN AND MAKE SPECIAL 'LUNCH-BOXES' FOR ADULTS

Textiles Technology

MY PROJECT WAS TO DESIGN AND MAKE A T-SHIRT TO HELP LAUNCH A NEW COMPUTER GAME

WHAT DO PEOPLE LIKE TO EAT FOR LUNCH?

Excuse me! I wonder if you could tell me...

SURVEY
How many times a week do you eat sandwiches at lunchtime? 2, 3, 2, 2, 1, 1, 3, 2, 1

What fillings do you like?
Cheese ⁺⁺⁺ ⁺⁺⁺ ||
Salad ⁺⁺⁺ ||

WHERE COULD I GET MY INFORMATION FROM?

- How can I find out what sizes T-shirts are?
- Where can I find examples of suitable images and colours?
- How can I discover what sorts of designs are most popular?

I APPLIED THE INFORMATION I DISCOVERED

Many people seem to want a lunch which:

- they can eat quickly
- is inexpensive
- is low-fat
- is suitable for vegetarians.

Dhal, onion, pea and tomato samosa?

Beetroot salad?

Chocolate and orange muffin?

THIS HELPED GIVE ME SOME IDEAS

SIMQUEST

SQ

From my first designs I think the 'explosion' design below would be most popular as it is bright and bold.

HOW MANY? HOW MUCH?

Home made baps with vegetable tikka?

Banana Slice?
2 bananas, 225g flour?

Apple and nut salad?
What quantities of apples and nuts?

I EXPERIMENTED WITH DIFFERENT TECHNIQUES

How can the motif be applied?
Dyes
✓ Appliqué
✓ Fabric paint

SQ

WHAT DO I KNOW ABOUT HEALTHY EATING?

For a meal to be balanced I know it must contain all the necessary nutrients. It should also contain healthy ingredients. It would be a good idea to consult the nutritional database.

Nutrients

Nutrients CD

WHICH TOOLS AND PROCESSES WOULD BE BEST?

I tested different materials, dyes and colour combinations.

If I use an overlocking machine the seams will be strong, flexible and have a smart finish.

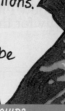

WILL IT APPEAL TO DIFFERENT PEOPLE?

The samosa lunch box is high in fat. It needs to be made lower in fat to appeal more to those who want to be healthy.

For people eating on the move the tikka lunch box might be messy to eat. Maybe I could change its shape?

DOES THE DESIGN DO EVERYTHING IT SHOULD?

DESIGN CHECK
The design relates to the game.
I will be able to make up the design at school.
The design looks exciting and colourful
appeal to a people

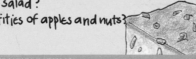

Designing: Level 5

MY PROJECT WAS TO DESIGN AND MAKE A FUSE TESTER

To achieve Level 5 I will need to:

Investigate

❏ Find out more about the situation or circumstances in which my product will be used. This needs to be done outside school.
❏ Study a range of existing solutions.

Date: Project: Teacher:

Have good ideas

❏ Adapt what I have discovered about the way existing designs work, what they are made from, how they are put together and what they look like.
❏ Show my ideas to someone else and discuss them. Record what they said and if and how I changed my ideas as a result.

Date: Project: Teacher:

Develop my design

❏ Use a variety of words, drawings, measurements and models to help me to develop my ideas about the shapes, materials, components and methods of construction I might use.
❏ Include as much detail as possible.

Date: Project: Teacher:

Apply what I know

❏ Use what I have learnt about different materials, tools and components in other D&T project work.
❏ Make it clear how I have used this knowledge in my designing.

Date: Project: Teacher:

Evaluate

❏ Comment on how well my design might or might not work in use.
❏ Make notes about how the tools and materials and the time I have might limit what I can do.

Date: Project: Teacher:

AT HOME, I STUDIED SOME PRODUCTS THAT USED FUSES

How many fuses do we use? where would we keep a tester?

I BASED MY IDEAS ON AN EXISTING CIRCUIT

I studied some existing circuits and decided I could adapt this one to use for my tester.

I TRIED OUT SOME IDEAS USING SCRAP MATERIALS

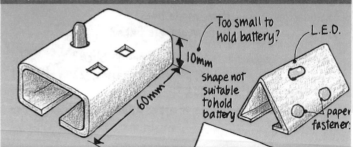

Too small to hold battery?

L.E.D.

10mm

60mm

shape not suitable to hold battery

paper fastener

WHAT MATERIALS WOULD BE BEST?

I could use some scrap materials to experiment with different shapes.

When I made a key ring last year I learnt how to shape and form acrylic. I could use this process again for my fuse tester.

HOW WELL DOES IT WORK?

I made up one of my designs full size to test it out. It worked but I discovered the battery was too loose and the circuit might easily get damaged.

Food Technology

MY PROJECT WAS TO DESIGN AND MAKE A NEW BREAD PRODUCT FOR A LOCAL RESTAURANT TO SERVE WITH ITS MEALS

WHERE CAN I FIND OUT MORE ABOUT HOW BREAD IS MADE?

Visit a bakery

Write to the Federation of Bakers

contact a manufacturer

Visit libraries

go to bakers, shops and supermarkets

WHAT FLAVOURS COULD I USE?

At my visit to a baker's I discovered the names of the different types of bread and the unusual ingredients which can be added to the mixture to produce interesting flavours.

I RECORDED MY IDEAS CAREFULLY

unusual square shape.

25g pinenuts

75 g chopped dried apricots

250g white strong flour

After eating an apricot and pinenut snack bar I thought this might make an interesting bread.

HOW CAN I GET THE TEXTURE RIGHT?

Last time I made bread I learnt it was important to use strong flour because of its high gluten content.

This is needed so that an elastic structure can be produced throughout the dough, making a light, textured loaf.

WHAT PROBLEMS COULD THERE BE?

Even if I use easy-blend yeast it will take too much time to make a full-size loaf. Instead I will make small rolls which will bake more quickly.

Textiles Technology

MY PROJECT WAS TO DESIGN AND MAKE A QUILT FOR A LOCAL EXHIBITION ON THE THEME OF 'SEASONAL CHANGE'

THERE WERE MANY THINGS I NEEDED TO DISCOVER

I visited the gallery to find out:
• Where will my work be hung?
• Where will it be visible from?
• What colours are the surrounding walls?
• Where will artificial and natural light come from?

HOW GOOD WERE MY INITIAL IDEAS?

I showed my initial ideas to the exhibition organiser. She suggested the design should use larger pieces and bolder colours

I GOT DOWN TO DETAILS

I will need to make templates to exact sizes adding a seam allowance of 1.5cm.

Name each different shape and colour.

A
B
C
D

HOW COULD I STRENGTHEN THE FABRIC STRUCTURE?

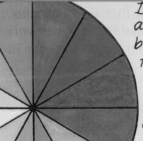

I will need to put a piece of fabric behind each piece to strengthen it.

I can use the colour wheel to choose warm and cold colours.

HOW LONG HAVE I GOT TO MAKE IT?

This design looks good on the computer but would take far too long to make.

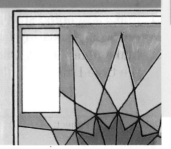

43

Designing: Level 6

To achieve Level 6 I will need to:

MY PROJECT WAS TO DESIGN AND MAKE A MECHANICAL DISPLAY DEVICE

Investigate

❏ Use a wide range of sources of information, including familiar products, situations and/or circumstances.

❏ Explain how this information will help me with my task.

Date: Project: Teacher:

Have good ideas

❏ Make sure I make some clear statements about the requirements for the appearance, function, safety and reliability of my product.

❏ Include details of the sort of people my product is intended for and where, when and how it is likely be used.

Date: Project: Teacher:

Develop my design

❏ Make at least one initial mock-up, prototype or trial-piece to help me develop and test out some specific aspects of my ideas.

❏ Choose some formal methods of presenting my ideas so that I can communicate my design proposals clearly and concisely.

Date: Project: Teacher:

Apply what I know

❏ Make it clear how I have used what I know about how existing products are made, and where, when and how they are used.

Date: Project: Teacher:

Evaluate

❏ Make a detailed study of the appearance and purpose of existing products that are similar to the one I am trying to design.

Date: Project: Teacher:

WHAT WOULD BE A GOOD SITUATION TO DESIGN FOR?

I decided to design and make a revolving display unit for a jewellery shop.

I consulted a CD-ROM to learn more about how different types of mechanisms work.

I DECIDED WHAT MY DESIGN HAD TO DO

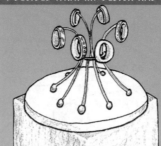

Requirements:
• suitable for displaying expensive jewellery
• needs to turn automatically for up to 8 hours a day
• must turn slowly - about 1 revolution every 30 seconds.

HOW CAN I SET UP SOME EXPERIMENTS?

I will try out different mechanisms using a construction kit.

LOOKING AT OTHER MECHANISMS WAS VERY HELPFUL

Working as a group we made a study of mechanisms used in every day products. I looked particularly at belt drivers to find out how they

HOW CAN I APPLY THESE IDEAS TO MY DESIGN?

worked and what they were made from. I was able to adapt one of the mechanisms to use in my design.

Food Technology

MY PROJECT WAS TO DESIGN AND MAKE A RANGE OF DISHES FOR SALE IN A LOCAL COMMUNITY CENTRE CANTEEN

Textiles Technology

MY PROJECT WAS TO DESIGN AND MAKE A HAT AS THE CENTRE-PIECE OF A SPECIAL SHOP-WINDOW DISPLAY

WHAT SIMILAR SITUATIONS COULD I INVESTIGATE?

I made a study of our school canteen. The results from my survey will help me to choose which sort of meals are the most popular.

I HAD TO FIND OUT ABOUT HATS AND WINDOW DISPLAYS

I made a study of some unusual hats and some shop-window displays. My designs will need to be eye-catching, hold the attention of potential customers and get them to come inside.

WHAT WILL PEOPLE WANT?

DESIGN CHECKLIST
- The meals must be suitable for the local community, vegetarians, those with food allergies, those concerned with healthy eating.
- The cost per portion must be between £1 and £1.50.
- Pre-preparation time must be between 30 and 40 minutes.

WHAT THEME SHOULD I CHOOSE?

I have chosen the theme of science fiction. I will design the window display and the hat.

I TRIED SEVERAL DIFFERENT RECIPES

① PRODUCT NAME
ingredients quantities
Sketch
equipment processes

② PRODUCT NAME
Ingredients
Equipment

I could also make a sample portion for the manager to try.

I NEEDED TO SORT OUT THE DETAILS

I can do some experiments with scrap materials on a dummy's head. I can check the balance and weight on a friend.

I also need to design a special logo for my design sheets.

HOW COULD I ADAPT AN EXISTING DISH?

My evaluation of a chicken curry from the school canteen suggested that it could be a better product if:

- the sauce was thicker
- the chicken pieces were cut smaller

Nutritional Analysis (per 100g)
Kcal = 190   Protein = 23.
Fat = 10

WHICH MATERIALS AND COMPONENTS SHOULD I USE?

KNITTED BOBBLE HAT: Wool is a yarn that breathes and keeps the wearer warm. It is easy to dye so comes in a large range of colours.

SO HOW DO YOU MAKE A CHICKEN CURRY?

- more curry powder was used to give a spicier taste.

...ates = 65g

Cost per portion
Estimated at £1.20

Taste
Not very hot
Rather sweet

Ingredients
Chicken

I LEARNT A LOT BY STUDYING SOME EXISTING HATS

STETSON: Stiff felt hat with a large brim that shades the wearer from the sun. The black cord goes under the chin to stop the hat falling off.

FANCY HAT: from the early 1800's straw base with feather 'wings' and fabric flowers.

Designing: Level 7

To achieve Level 7 I will need to:

Investigate

❑ Make it clear that I, rather than my teacher, identified the sources of information I needed to consult.
❑ Find out and explain about the different needs of a variety of people who might need or want to use my design idea.

Date: _____ Project: _____ Teacher: _____

Have good ideas

❑ Demonstrate how I have used my investigation and evaluation of existing products to help me develop my design ideas.
❑ Ensure I take into account the needs of a variety of potential users.

Date: _____ Project: _____ Teacher: _____

Develop my design

❑ Consider how the making of my design will affect the way it looks and works.
❑ Use a variety of media to communicate my design ideas to other people. Make sure I show the various features of my design, and how they will work in use.

Date: _____ Project: _____ Teacher: _____

Apply what I know

❑ Make it clear how I am using my skills of designing and making and my knowledge and understanding of materials and components, systems and control, existing products, quality and health and safety.

Date: _____ Project: _____ Teacher: _____

Evaluate

❑ When investigating existing products, try to find out about and explain why they look and work the way they do, and say how I think they were made.
❑ Write some clear statements to show that after evaluating the various stages of my work I have been able to decide what to do next.

Date: _____ Project: _____ Teacher: _____

Product Design

MY PROJECT WAS TO DESIGN AND MAKE A TOILETRIES GIFT PACK

I WORKED OUT WHAT I NEEDED TO INVESTIGATE

Diary   2nd June
As planned, I talked today to the local chemist about the toiletries he sold. He showed me a range of packages which

The display of goods on the shelf was clearly very important. He said he would stock gift packs that would attract customers.

SOMETHING FOR EVERYONE?

I decided to design a package for a set of baby toiletries for a new mum. It will also need to appeal to dads, grandparents and friends who would buy them as presents. I was inspired by some baby toys my neighbours' children had been given.

HOW COULD I MAKE IT?

If I used a blister pack it would help prevent the contents being tampered with but would it still look attractive?

WHICH WOULD BE THE BEST MATERIALS TO USE?

I discussed the problems of making the former in the shape of a teddy bear with my teacher. I will need to calculate the angles and surface area very carefully. He agreed that 0.5mm thick plastic film would be a good material to use.

I STUDIED SOME SIMILAR PACKAGING

PRODUCT ANALYSIS

Blister pack formed using wooden mould and industrial vacuum former.

Card backing printed separately using only two colours to reduce costs.

 ## Food Technology

MY PROJECT WAS TO DESIGN AND MAKE A RANGE OF NEW AND UNUSUAL MEALS SUITABLE FOR FREEZING

 ## Textiles Technology

MY PROJECT WAS TO DESIGN AND MAKE A SOFT TOY FOR THE CHILDREN'S WARD OF A LOCAL HOSPITAL

WHAT WOULD PEOPLE WANT?

I decided to interview a busy single mother, an elderly person and a young couple.

- The mother wanted something economical.
- The elderly person wanted something different.
- The young couple wanted something easy and quick to prepare.

IT SOON BECAME CLEAR WHAT WAS NEEDED

My ideas must:
- be quick to prepare
- be unusual
- be good value for money.

 I made a study of frozen foods in the supermarket and note that fish dishes were conventional and quite expensive.

WAS THERE A RECIPE I COULD ADAPT?

While looking through a recipe book I found a picture of 'Fish Florentine'. I will need to adapt it to make it more economical. Fish is also good as it retains its appearance well after defrosting.

I CONSIDERED WHAT I KNEW ABOUT HEATH AND SAFETY

My product will need to:
- be frozen between −18°C to −25°C
- be cooked at Gas mark 7 or 220°C
- use: 700g haddock, 300g spinach 100g cheese.

During preparation I must ensure the raw fish is kept away from the other ingredients.

I ASKED OTHER PEOPLE TO EVALUATE MY MEAL

I made up a sample of the fish pie and asked some tasters to complete a star diagram.

I discovered that I needed to find a way of making the pie more moist and cheesy.

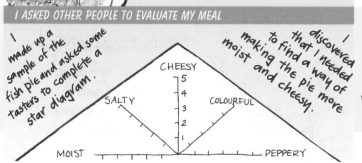

I CONTACTED THE LOCAL HOSPITAL

STAFF
1. Age range of children.
2. Storage facilities.
3. Hygiene.
4. Other toys available.

Dear Sir/Madam, I am designing and making a soft toy for your childrens' ward as a D+T project. It would be useful if I...

I NEEDED SOME INSPIRATION!

CHILDREN
1. Favourite colours.
2. Favourite characters
3. Favourite toys and games.
4. Sizes

The answers I got from the staff and children helped to give me some ideas.

I SHOWED MY IDEAS TO SOME CHILDREN

The materials I use to join the limbs will affect the appearance of my design.

HOW CAN I APPLY MY KNOWLEDGE AND UNDERSTANDING?

LEG, ARM, HEAD, BODY, NECK

I can use what I know about cutting and drafting paper patterns to create a 3D representation of my design.

HOW ARE SOFT TOYS MADE?

I took an old rag doll apart to learn more about joining the parts together and the order of construction.

contd.
3. Join the arms
4. Join the legs
5. Make th clothe...

47

Designing: Level 8

To achieve Level 8 I will need to:

Product Design

MY PROJECT WAS TO DESIGN AND MAKE A SOIL-MOISTURE TESTER

Investigate

❏ Make sure I identify a wide range of conflicting demands on my designs.

Date: Project: Teacher:

Have good ideas

❏ Use a range of techniques (e.g. brainstorming, using analogies and transformations) to help me generate appropriate ideas.

Date: Project: Teacher:

Develop my design

❏ Draw on my investigation and evaluation of existing products to help inform and justify the development of my ideas.
❏ Communicate how my ideas solve the conflicting demands I have identified.

Date: Project: Teacher:

Apply what I know

❏ Show how the decisions I am making about which materials and techniques to use are based on my knowledge of their physical and working characteristics.

Date: Project: Teacher:

Evaluate

❏ Explain when describing and evaluating existing products how they have been designed to meet the needs and preferences of a variety of users.

Date: Project: Teacher:

THERE WAS A LOT I NEEDED TO FIND OUT ABOUT

My design will need to be:
• visible, but not too intrusive
• audible, but not too loud
• durable, but not last forever!
• safe, but use electronic componants
• waterproof, because the plant will be watered.

I TRIED SIMPLIFYING SOME ANIMAL SHAPES

I could base the shape on a frog

The eyes, legs and feet are the most distinctive features

HOW COULD I ADAPT AN EXISTING PRODUCT?

• I could use one of the LEDs to check the battery level and the other for the soil moisture content.
• I could add a push-to-make switch which would close the circuit to check the battery.

HOW CAN I ENSURE MY MOULD WILL FORM WELL?

I could use A.B.S. as it forms to a high definition. The sides of the mould must slope by an angle of at least 3°. It must have small diameter holes drilled through to allow the air to be expelled.

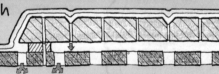

HOW COULD EXISTING PRODUCTS BE IMPROVED?

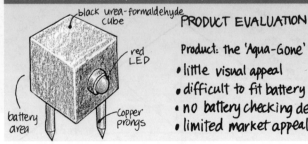

black urea-formaldehyde cube

red LED

battery area

copper prongs

PRODUCT EVALUATION

Product: the 'Aqua-Gone'
• little visual appeal
• difficult to fit battery
• no battery checking device
• limited market appeal.

Food Technology

MY PROJECT WAS TO DESIGN AND MAKE FOOD PRODUCTS FOR A THEMED RESTAURANT

Textiles Technology

MY PROJECT WAS TO DESIGN AND MAKE MASKS FOR A PLAY ABOUT THE FALL OF THE AZTECS

EVERYONE LIKES SOMETHING DIFFERENT...

I have discovered that families often find it difficult to please everyone from a single menu. !£ ?

Some people want a big meal while others just want a snack. Some want something traditional while others want something more adventurous.

Children prefer familiar dishes which are easy to eat

THIS WAS GOING TO BE DEMANDING

The mask should:
- be faithful to the shapes and colours of the Aztecs but not be just a copy.
- be suitable for the actors to wear for long periods under hot lights.
- not hamper the actors' performance.

ONE THING QUICKLY LED TO ANOTHER

Video screens showing films

Food named after stars

Stars' favourite foods

Posters of film stars on wall

Unusual menu design

Film Stars' Restaurant - take - away

DISCUSSING THE PROBLEMS PROVIDED SOME INSIGHTS AND IDEAS

- reflect the character the actor is portraying.

Aztec shapes could be used to symbolise eyes, nose and mouth.

Aztec temple shapes could symbolise the importance of their religious beliefs.

HOW COULD I USE STANDARD COMPONENTS?

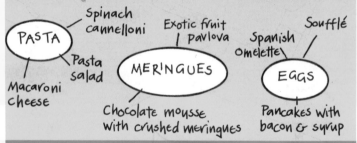

PASTA
- Spinach cannelloni
- Pasta salad
- Macaroni cheese

MERINGUES
- Exotic fruit Pavlova
- Chocolate mousse with crushed meringues

EGGS
- Souffle
- Spanish omelette
- Pancakes with bacon & syrup

I NEEDED SOME FEEDBACK ON MY DESIGNS

I presented my ideas at the next production meeting.

These are delicate materials but they are light and strong enough to last for the total number of performances.

I designed masks that would not hamper the actors' performance, especially speech.

WHAT DO I KNOW ABOUT HOW TO USE EGGS?

EGGS:

To make the souffle the eggs will need to be whisked to trap lots of air.

In the spanish omelette the protein in the eggs will help the omelette to set.

The eggs will need to be beaten into milk to make the batter for the pancakes.

I WORKED OUT WHICH MATERIALS WOULD BE BEST

Stiffened fabrics applied to a chicken wire base will be strong and light.

I will use 'size', a strong glue used to strengthen theatre flats.

SIZE

HOW DO RESTAURANTS MEET THEIR CUSTOMERS' NEEDS?

In the restaurant I visited, I saw how they had planned three different menus to cater for a wide range of tastes. By using standard components, preparation time had been reduced and bulk purchases had cut costs.

I STUDIED MASKS FROM OTHER TIMES AND CULTURES

African ritual masks were used to inspire fear! Graphic, bold shapes heighten the impact.

Eighteenth century ladies' masks were used as a token disguise to maintain their social reputation.

Making: Levels 1 and 2

To achieve Levels 1 and 2 I will need to:

Product Design

MY PROJECT WAS TO DESIGN AND MAKE A PULL-ALONG TOY FOR A YOUNG CHILD

Plan the making

❏ Tell or show other people what I am going to make, and what I am going to make it with.
❏ Make a list of the materials and tools I will need to use.

Date: Project: Teacher:

I WROTE DOWN WHAT I WOULD NEED

Tools

I will need to use:
• a coping saw to cut out the duck
• a drill to make the eye and the holes for the axles.

Materials

• 15mm ply
• 4 x 50mm wheels
• 2 x 30mm dowel rods

Apply what I know

❏ Choose the best available materials for making my product.
❏ Say why I have chosen them.

Date: Project: Teacher:

WOOD, METAL OR PLASTIC?

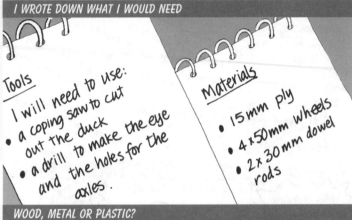

I will choose plywood because it won't warp and is very tough.

Work with materials

❏ Cut, shape and join together the materials.
❏ Try to use more than one way of joining materials.
❏ Say how I will use my tools safely.

Date: Project: Teacher:

I CUT THE WOOD AND CAREFULLY USED THE DRILL

Evaluate my final product

❏ Say if what I made looked and worked as I wanted it to.
❏ Say if I chose the best material. What other materials might have been better?
❏ Say what is good about the product I have designed and made. How could it be improved?

Date: Project: Teacher:

IS MY DESIGN A SUCCESS?

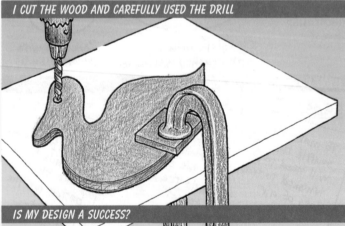

I think my wooden toy looks good. If the wheels were thicker it might not fall over so easily.

Food Technology

MY PROJECT WAS TO DESIGN AND MAKE SOME ANIMAL BISCUITS TO EAT WITH FRIENDS AT BREAK-TIME

Textiles Technology

MY PROJECT WAS TO DESIGN AND MAKE FINGER-PUPPETS BASED ON A FAIRY TALE

I EXPLAINED HOW I WAS GOING TO MAKE MY BISCUITS

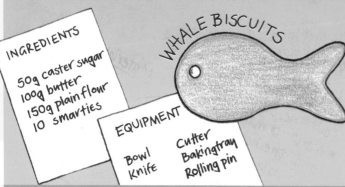

WHALE BISCUITS

INGREDIENTS
50g caster sugar
100g butter
150g plain flour
10 smarties

EQUIPMENT
Bowl
Knife
Cutter
Bakingtray
Rolling pin

I MADE A LIST OF TOOLS AND MATERIALS

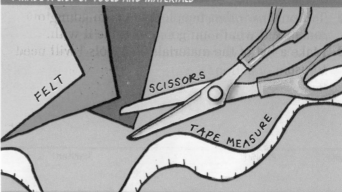

FELT
SCISSORS
TAPE MEASURE

WHAT MIXTURE WILL BE BEST?

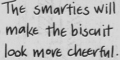

I have chosen to use shortbread because I can easily roll out the mixture.

The smarties will make the biscuit look more cheerful.

WHICH COLOURS OF FELT SHOULD I USE?

I will use bright colours for my puppets to make them more attractive to young children.

SAFETY FIRST!

I must wear oven gloves when using the oven.

HOW CAN I JOIN THE MATERIALS TOGETHER?

I made sure the scissors were left closed when I wasn't using them.

I joined the pieces of my puppet with thread. I tried using string but it didn't work.

Glue can be used for sticking on details like eyes + hands.

GLU

HOW COULD MY PRODUCT BE IMPROVED?

My biscuits worked well. My friends and I enjoyed eating them. Next time I will grease the baking tin properly to stop them sticking.

DID I USE THE BEST MATERIALS?

The hair was too difficult to make in felt so I made it in wool.

I made up a story for some primary school children. They enjoyed the show.

Making: Level 3

To achieve Level 3 I will need to:

Plan the making

❑ Sort out the main steps involved in making my design and put them in the right order.
❑ Write a list or draw a simple flow-diagram to show my plan of action.

Date: Project: Teacher:

WHAT ORDER DO I NEED TO MAKE THINGS IN?

1. Make cat template
2. Stick to copper
3. Cut out
4. File edges

Apply what I know

❑ Decide for myself which are the best tools and materials to use for each job I need to do.

Date: Project: Teacher:

WHICH TOOLS WILL I NEED TO USE?

- Snips to cut out cat shape
- Files – half round and flat
- Wet and dry paper

Work with materials

❑ Use the tools carefully to cut, shape, form, mould and/or mix the materials.
❑ Be as accurate as I can with my measuring and making.
❑ Use simple finishing techniques.

Date: Project: Teacher:

I USED THE TOOLS WITH CARE

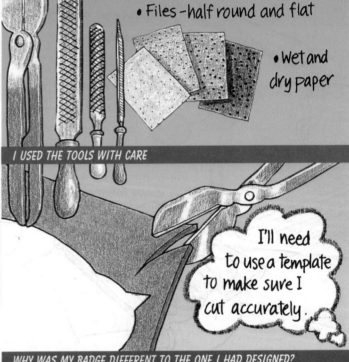

I'll need to use a template to make sure I cut accurately.

Evaluate my final product

❑ Check to see if what I made is different from my final design.
❑ Explain how it is different and why I needed to change it.

Date: Project: Teacher:

WHY WAS MY BADGE DIFFERENT TO THE ONE I HAD DESIGNED?

I realised that my cat can't have whiskers as they would be too fragile and might break off.

Food Technology

MY PROJECT WAS TO DESIGN AND MAKE A RANGE OF LOW-COST HEALTHY MEALS USING FRUIT

Textiles Technology

MY PROJECT WAS TO DESIGN AND MAKE A BAG TO CARRY ART MATERIALS. IT HAD TO USE NATURAL FIBRES AND HAVE AN AFRICAN THEME

WHAT ARE THE MAIN STEPS?

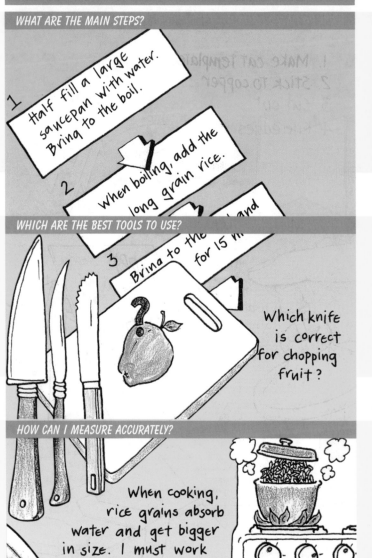

1. Half fill a large saucepan with water. Bring to the boil.

2. When boiling, add the long grain rice.

3. Bring to the and for 15 m...

WHICH ARE THE BEST TOOLS TO USE?

Which knife is correct for chopping fruit?

HOW CAN I MEASURE ACCURATELY?

When cooking, rice grains absorb water and get bigger in size. I must work out exactly how much rice I need per portion.

WHY DID I NEED TO CHANGE MY DESIGN?

In my final product I did not use wild rice as it cost too much. I added some brown rice to increase the fibre. I also used the pineapple juice as a dressing.

WHAT NEEDS TO BE DONE FIRST?

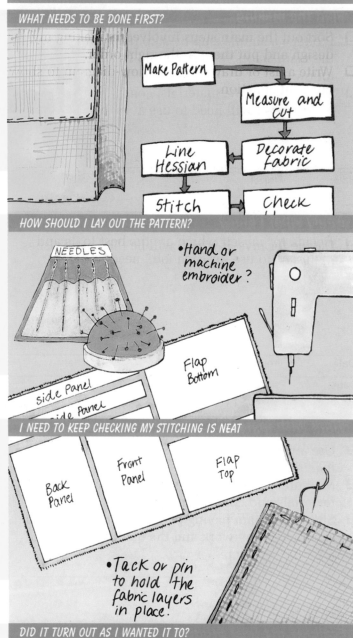

Make Pattern → Measure and cut

Line Hessian ← Decorate fabric

Stitch → Check

HOW SHOULD I LAY OUT THE PATTERN?

NEEDLES

• Hand or machine embroider?

Flap Bottom

Side Panel

Side Panel

I NEED TO KEEP CHECKING MY STITCHING IS NEAT

Back Panel

Front Panel

Flap Top

• Tack or pin to hold the fabric layers in place.

DID IT TURN OUT AS I WANTED IT TO?

• I made the bag slightly bigger to fit an A4 sketch book.

• The embroidery was not as effective as an appliqué.

53

Making: Level 4

To achieve Level 4 I will need to:

MY PROJECT WAS TO DESIGN AND MAKE A 'POP-UP' GREETINGS CARD

Plan the making

- ❏ Produce a simple step-by-step plan or diagram of the main stages in making that I will need to follow.
- ❏ Make a list of the materials, components and techniques I will need to use at each stage.

Date: Project: Teacher:

WHAT DO I NEED TO DO FIRST?

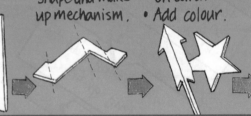

STAGE 1
- Mark out card.
- Cut card.

STAGE 2
- Fold card to shape and make up mechanism.

STAGE 3
- Draw graphics on card.
- Add colour.

Apply what I know

- ❏ Decide for myself which will be the best finishes to use.

Date: Project: Teacher:

HOW SHOULD I FINISH IT?

I will need to use a fixative to stop the pastel and paint from smudging.

HAPPY BIRTHDAY

Work with materials

- ❏ Use a variety of materials and techniques of making.
- ❏ Measure, mark out, cut, shape and join my materials and components together.
- ❏ Show how I am paying particular attention to the accuracy of my work and the quality of finish of my final product.

MY CUTTING AND SCORING HAS TO BE NEAT

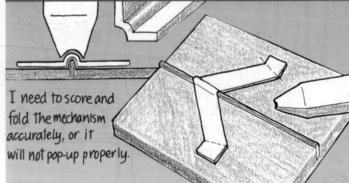

I need to score and fold the mechanism accurately, or it will not pop-up properly.

Evaluate my final product

Write down a list of the features of my product that work well or do not work as well I had hoped.

Date: Project: Teacher:

WHAT DO OTHER PEOPLE THINK OF MY DESIGN?

FINAL EVALUATION
- The star is too big and sticks out of the side of the card when closed.
- Lots of people say they like the design and would want one for someone's birthday.

Food Technology

MY PROJECT WAS TO DESIGN AND MAKE SPECIAL 'LUNCH-BOXES' FOR ADULTS

Textiles Technology

MY PROJECT WAS TO DESIGN AND MAKE A T-SHIRT TO HELP LAUNCH A NEW COMPUTER GAME

WHAT INGREDIENTS WILL I NEED?

Making the bap

Stage 1. Collect and weigh out the ingredients:

- 100g wholemeal strong flour
- 150g white strong flour
- 15g butter
- ½ sachet of easyblend yeast
- 1 ascorbic acid tablet
- 150 ml warm milk
- 1 teaspoon sugar

WHAT WILL GIVE THE BEST FINISH?

I decided to use an egg glaze. This will give a shiny finish.

I will need to wrap the finished product in cling-film to keep it fresh.

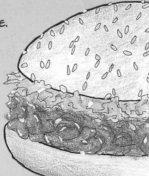

THERE WAS A LOT TO DO

creaming the banana slices

kneading the bread

stirring the stir-fry

making the mayonnaise

I WROTE A SHORT PROJECT REPORT

I was very pleased with the tikka baps. To make them quicker and easier to eat I made the bottom of the bun larger.

The apple and nut salad tastes good, but might be a problem for people with a nut allergy.

I NEEDED A STEP-BY-STEP PLAN

Measure and make T-shirt pattern.

Lay out and cut.

Apply motif.

WHAT DO I KNOW ABOUT HOW TO GET A GOOD FINISH?

Remember to fix the fabric paint using an iron. Protect the design with a cloth.

Machine together.

Finish seams.

I WANTED SOMETHING THAT WAS WELL MADE

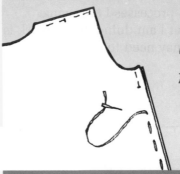

I will pin and tack when making up, for a more accurate result.

HOW SUCCESSFUL IS MY FINAL DESIGN?

- ☑ STRONG, CLEAR DESIGN THAT APPEALS TO EVERYONE.
- ☑ THE SIZE FITS THE MAJORITY OF PEOPLE.
- ☒ THE SMALLER LETTERS ARE HARD TO READ.

Making: Level 5

Product Design

MY PROJECT WAS TO DESIGN AND MAKE A FUSE TESTER

To achieve Level 5 I will need to:

Plan the making

- ❏ Follow closely the plans I have made.
- ❏ Change my plans if things don't work out quite as expected.
- ❏ Make a note of any changes I need to make, and say why.

Date: Project: Teacher:

SOME THINGS DID NOT QUITE GO TO PLAN

When I was making the tester I realised that the resistor would need to be soldered beneath the board as it gets in the way when it is put inside the casing.

Apply what I know

- ❏ Use my past knowledge of working with tools, materials and processes to help achieve a high level of finish and accuracy.

Date: Project: Teacher:

HOW CAN I IMPROVE ITS FINISH?

I need to buff the edges to get a good finish using a soft mop and acrylic polish.

Work with materials

- ❏ Make sure I am following safety precautions with the materials, tools and processes I am using.
- ❏ Measure and check what I am doing. If my work is not accurate enough I may need to do it again.

Date: Project: Teacher:

WHAT SAFETY PRECAUTIONS MUST I TAKE?

I must remember to wear goggles when using the buffing machine and to hold my work well below the centre spindle.

Evaluate my final product

- ❏ Compare what I have made with my design proposal.
- ❏ Suggest some ways in which I might be able to improve my final product if it does not look and work as I intended

Date: Project: Teacher:

I GOT A USER TO TEST MY PRODUCT

PERFORMANCE CHECKLIST
Can you use it easily?
Is it strong enough?
Can you change the battery?
Do you like the way it

EVALUATION
My test results showed that it worked well and the battery is easy to change. However it does not look very attractive and the battery is not well ... tected ... casing could ... plasti...

Food Technology

MY PROJECT WAS TO DESIGN AND MAKE A NEW BREAD PRODUCT FOR A LOCAL RESTAURANT TO SERVE WITH ITS MEALS

WHAT MIGHT GO WRONG?

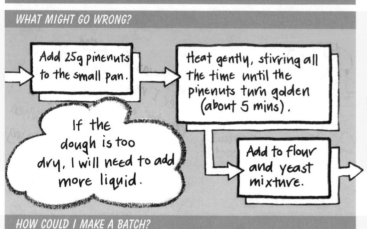

Add 25g pinenuts to the small pan.

Heat gently, stirring all the time until the pinenuts turn golden (about 5 mins).

Add to flour and yeast mixture.

If the dough is too dry, I will need to add more liquid.

HOW COULD I MAKE A BATCH?

To produce a light textured bread I must:
- knead thoroughly
- allow time for the dough to prove.

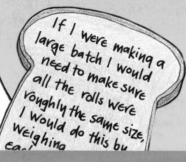

If I were making a large batch I would need to make sure all the rolls were roughly the same size, I would do this by weighing ea... piece of dough accurately.

ACCURACY IS IMPORTANT

Check dough is ready for shaping.

Time the baking to the nearest minute.

HOW WELL DOES MY DESIGN SOLVE THE PROBLEM?

I was very pleased with the flavour of my bread. It is unusual because it is both sweet and nutty.

It should complement a wide variety of needs in the restaurant.

Textiles Technology

MY PROJECT WAS TO DESIGN AND MAKE A QUILT FOR A LOCAL EXHIBITION ON THE THEME OF 'SEASONAL CHANGE'

I MAY NEED TO CHANGE SOME OF MY PLANS

Separate the pieces according to type.
- Check pieces and colours will fit together as intended. I might need to remake some of the pieces if they don't fit.

HOW CAN I APPLY WHAT I KNOW?

✓ Iron backing to each piece to avoid slipping as I sew.

✓ Press seams as I go.

QUALITY COUNTS!

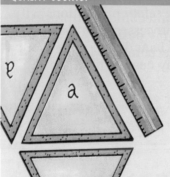

✓ Make sure seam allowances are straight.

✓ Make sure that the pieces of the same type are all of an identical size.

WHAT COULD I HAVE DONE TO IMPROVE MY DESIGN?

✓ The change of colour around the design works well.

✗ The seasons could have been shown more clearly.

✗ I should have tried more fabrics of different textures.

✓ the organiser was delighted and put it in the exhibition.

Making: Level 6

Product Design

MY PROJECT WAS TO DESIGN AND MAKE A MECHANICAL DISPLAY DEVICE

To achieve Level 6 I will need to:

Plan the making

- ❏ Look carefully at my plans and identify where any difficulties might occur.
- ❏ Suggest what I would do if I did find a problem at a particular stage.

Date: Project: Teacher:

WHAT PROBLEMS MIGHT I HAVE?

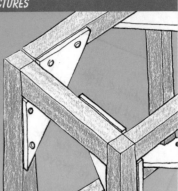

My design was based on using a small motor. However I discovered there were no more of these in stock and it could be at least three weeks before any more will come in. If they don't arrive by the 15th I will have to use a large motor instead and make the box larger to fit.

Apply what I know

- ❏ Build on what I have learnt in the past about how to work with a variety of tools, materials and components.

Date: Project: Teacher:

I APPLIED MY KNOWLEDGE OF STRUCTURES

From the project I did last year I know I will need to strengthen the frame joints. I intend to use the principal of triangulation to help produce a more stable structure.

Work with materials

- ❏ Practise using a particular technique or process I am going to use to make my design.
- ❏ Concentrate on being as accurate as I can.

Date: Project: Teacher:

MY WORK NEEDED TO BE NEAT AND PRECISE

turntable

nylon washer

0.5mm

rotation spindle

To make sure the display stand turns smoothly the hole at the top of the rotating frame will have to be accurate to a tolerance of ±1mm.

Evaluate my final product

- ❏ Test my final product out in use to find out how well it works.
- ❏ Say how it might be improved.

Date: Project: Teacher:

SO HOW WELL DOES MY DESIGN WORK?

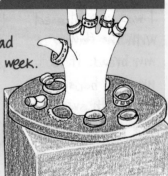

I took the display stand to a jewellers' shop where they had agreed to test it for me for a week. They said the batteries only lasted two days before they needed replacing. I will therefore need to use a mains transformer instead.

Food Technology

MY PROJECT WAS TO DESIGN AND MAKE A RANGE OF DISHES FOR SALE IN A LOCAL COMMUNITY CENTRE CANTEEN

Textiles Technology

MY PROJECT WAS TO DESIGN AND MAKE A HAT AS THE CENTRE-PIECE OF A SPECIAL SHOP-WINDOW DISPLAY

WHAT MIGHT GO WRONG?

- I must ensure the chicken is properly cooked by checking the juices run clear.

- Rice can go cold very quickly. I need to find a way to keep it hot without it drying out.

CAN I OBTAIN THE MATERIALS I NEED IN TIME?

I will need to buy the following things in advance:
Fire resistant spray
Metallic spray paint
Thin plastic tubing
Round beads
Head band

WHAT COOKING METHODS DO I KNOW ABOUT?

A quick and energy saving way of cooking the chicken would be to microwave it.

To stop lumps forming it is essential to keep stirring the sauce as it is heated. This will keep the thickening agent evenly mixed in the liquid.

WHICH TOOLS AND PROCESSES SHOULD I USE?

Head band
Foam covering fabric
GLU

Traditional methods of construction such as hand sewing will need to be mixed with more unusual ones.

I REALISED I WOULD NEED TO:

Fry 1 large chopped onion for 3 to 4 minutes.
Pour 300ml of boiling water onto a stock cube.
Weigh out exactly 150g of rice.

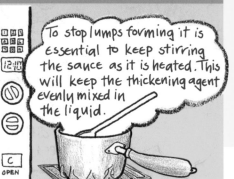

PRACTICE MAKES PERFECT!

covering the wires with fabric.

I will have to practise all the techniques I will use to make the hat.

I must keep checking that the hat still fits.

THE FINAL TEST – WHAT DO PEOPLE THINK?

I set up a taste-testing session in which I gave a sample of the curry to various people to get their opinion.

① Was it spicy enough?   5/10
② Did it taste like a traditional curry?   6/10
③ Did it look appetising?   4/10

HOW CAN I TEST OUT MY DESIGN?

The hat needs to be even bigger and more colourful to be eye-catching. A friend of mine wants to wear it to a party.

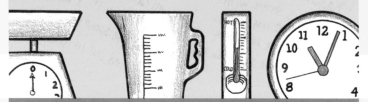

Making: Level 7

To achieve Level 7 I will need to:

Product Design

MY PROJECT WAS TO DESIGN AND MAKE A TOILETRIES GIFT PACK

Plan the making

❑ Include an estimate in my plans of how long it should take me to carry out the main stages I have identified.

❑ Modify my plans as necessary to ensure I complete my making.

Date: Project: Teacher:

Apply what I know

❑ Carefully match what I know about the characteristics and properties of materials and components with the tools, equipment and processes I know will be available for me to use.

Date: Project: Teacher:

Work with materials

❑ Write down if and why I needed to change my design or the way I planned to make it.

Date: Project: Teacher:

Evaluate my final product

❑ Decide which aspects of my design I want to test.

❑ Work out which methods of testing are most likely to supply the specific information I need.

❑ Make simple and quick changes to see if they make the design work better.

Date: Project: Teacher:

HOW CAN I GET IT FINISHED IN TIME?

STAGE	TASK	ESTIMATED TIME
3	Cut out plastic shapes	1 hour Fri a.m.
4	Prepare card artwork	2 hours Mon p.m.
5	Print backing card	1½ hours Wed p.m.
6	Mould teddy bears	2 hours Fri a.m.

WHERE ARE THE WEAKEST POINTS LIKELY TO BE?

VIBROSAW

The plastic will be brittle after heating and be difficult to cut. I will need to be careful.

WHY DID I CHANGE THE DESIGN?

Diary

I had planned to cut the teddy bears shape with a scalpel, but my teacher suggested a vibrosaw. I shall have to finish the edge of the formed acrylic very carefully by hand as the buffing mop will catch on the edge and might break it. I wonder how the same process is carried out in industry?

WHAT DO I NEED TO TEST?

TESTING, TESTING....

I plan to:

• show the pack to a range of people who might buy it to get their comments

• take it to the chemist to ask if he thinks it is good enough for display

• test the hanging device – is it strong enough?

Food Technology

MY PROJECT WAS TO DESIGN AND MAKE A RANGE OF NEW AND UNUSUAL MEALS SUITABLE FOR FREEZING

HOW LONG WILL EACH STAGE TAKE?

PRODUCT: Fish Florentine

Stage	Time	Production steps
3	11:20	While fish is poaching, make topping from bread and parsley using food processor.
4	11.35	Start to prepare cheese sauce; melt butter in saucepan.
5	11.45	Stir in milk and gently add

SAFETY FIRST....

It would be dangerous to use a foil container in a microwave! Instead I will need to use a heat-resistant plastic container which can be put in the freezer and a microwave oven.

HOW COULD I IMPROVE IT?

There seems to be a lot of oil on the surface.

Note: Sauce
Change to a blended fat-less sauce using cornflour. There's too much fat in the dish with butter and cheese.

WHAT TEST METHODS SHOULD I USE?

I want to test if the cooking times I am proposing for a microwave and an oven are accurate.

I will use a hedonic rating sensory evaluation technique with a group of testers to assess how well different samples have cooked.

Very wel...
Well cooke...
Quite well c...
Just cooked
A little un...
Und...

Textiles Technology

MY PROJECT WAS TO DESIGN AND MAKE A SOFT TOY FOR THE CHILDREN'S WARD OF A LOCAL HOSPITAL

WHAT ARE THE MAIN STEPS?

CUTTING
☐ Body   1hr
☐ Limbs   1hr
☐ Shoes   ½hr
          Total 2½hrs

MAKING
☐ Sew body   1hr
☐ Padding   1hr
☐ Add limbs   1hr
☐ Sew on eye

Buy Padding

Is it easier to attach shoes first?

WHICH MATERIALS WILL WORK BEST?

For the shoes and other details I will use felt, which will not fray.

I know that calico will be strong enough for the limbs and not too thick to sew

NOT EVERYTHING WENT ACCORDING TO PLAN

It is very hard to attach the limbs to the fur body.

I must think of another way of attaching the limbs. Maybe I should sew them to the body when it is flat and then finish off the body later.

WHAT COULD I TRY CHANGING?

I wanted to find out if the joints would take the strain. I gave the toy to my sister and her friends

When I got it back I checked the seams. Where they had come apart I finished the seams more securely.

61

Making: Level 8

Product Design

MY PROJECT WAS TO DESIGN AND MAKE A SOIL-MOISTURE TESTER

To achieve Level 8 I will need to:

Plan the making

❏ Show in my plans for making when and where I will have to take some key decisions about which materials, tools and processes to use.

❏ Suggest what the alternatives might be.

Date: Project: Teacher:

Apply what I know

❏ Ensure I know how to use the materials and tools needed in the most effective way.

Date: Project: Teacher:

Work with materials

❏ Check that I have the necessary skills to use the most effective techniques of making.

❏ Organise my tools and materials so that I can make my product as accurately and precisely as possible.

Date: Project: Teacher:

Evaluate my final product

❏ Discuss any aspects of my design which were not covered in my original proposal, such as environmental, social and cultural issues associated with my design.

Date: Project: Teacher:

I USED A COMPUTER TO HELP MY PLANNING

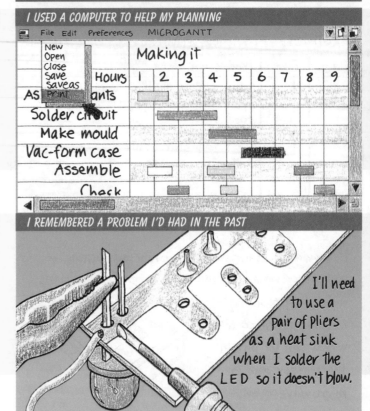

I REMEMBERED A PROBLEM I'D HAD IN THE PAST

I'll need to use a pair of pliers as a heat sink when I solder the LED so it doesn't blow.

SOME THINGS WERE NEW TO ME

Last time I did an electronics project I made a PCB using copper-coated board. This time I shall use stripboard, but I need to find out more about how to use it and try it out first.

HOW COULD THE DESIGN BE IMPROVED?

I am concerned that my design is not very environmentally friendly as it is made from plastic. I also need to look at ways of reducing the manufacturing cost for batch production.

Food Technology

MY PROJECT WAS TO DESIGN AND MAKE FOOD PRODUCTS FOR A THEMED RESTAURANT

SEVERAL THINGS COULD BE DONE AT THE SAME TIME

PASTA PRE-PRODUCTION SCHEDULE

- Macaroni cheese
- Pasta salad
- Cook 200g Pasta
- Prepare sauce
- Drain pasta and divide in two
- Add sauce to pasta
- Prepare vegetables

I KNOW HOW TO MAKE GOOD MERINGUES

To make the meringues, egg-whites must be whisked in a clean, grease-free bowl. They should be whisked until they form peaks.

Over whisking causes the structure of the egg-white to lose its stability.

CAREFUL PREPARATION IS ESSENTIAL

I must:
- check fridge temperature is 5°C
- place ingredients and tools where they are easily accessible and organised according to their use
- identify stages in production where hygiene checks need to be made.

HOW COULD THE PRODUCTS BE MADE IN QUANTITY?

I produced a detailed report on my project, discussing the good and bad points of my product and the development process I had used.

The production methods I used to make my dishes would be very similar to those needed by the restaurant, though the quantities would be larger.

Textiles Technology

MY PROJECT WAS TO DESIGN AND MAKE MASKS FOR A PLAY ABOUT THE FALL OF THE AZTECS

MY SCHEDULE HAD TO FIT IN WITH EVERYONE ELSE'S

The production team met to plan when everything was needed for.

My masks are required by the 25th. I will need to make the basic mask frames and then adapt them in discussion with the director and actors during the final rehearsals.

WHAT IS THE MOST EFFECTIVE METHOD OF PRODUCTION?

To make all the masks in time I will need to set up a small production line, like the one we tried last term.
It will save a lot of time if I make a proper mould which the pieces of wire can be shaped round.

WORKER 1 — Make mould
WORKER 2 — Cut wire
WORKER 3 — Soak fabric
Shape wire to mould

WHICH STAGES WILL NEED TO BE CHECKED?

The edges will need to be checked to make sure they are properly bound.

Bind wire
Inspect bind
Check eye and mouth sizes
Add fabric

The measurements for the mouth and the eye openings will each need to be checked against the specification.

AFTER THE DRESS-REHEARSAL

In scene 3 the lighting didn't work on the mask, so it will have to be resprayed.
One mask was too tall to get through a door-way; the set designer will sort this out.

The director said he felt that my masks added to the portrayal of a culture on the brink of destruction.

63

Design and Making
Exceptional Performance

To achieve Exceptional Performance I will need to:

❏ Produce design ideas that include a greater depth and breadth of work in all aspects of the Attainment Targets.

❏ Provide details that indicate how my product could be manufactured in quantity.

❏ Make the best use of the available time and resources.

❏ Ensure what I make is appropriately precise, reliable and durable, as specified in my proposal.

❏ Devise evaluation procedures to help indicate ways of improving my design, and re-make what I have done to implement them.

SAFE STOPPING DISTANCE DISPLAY

Gemma Wicks won an award for her design for an electronic product to help prevent accidents.

'My project was to help prevent motorway pile-ups. These happen because most drivers do not leave enough distance between themselves and the vehicle in front. Therefore when breaking suddenly there is not enough time and space for the following vehicle to brake, making a collision almost inevitable. This is likely to happen again to the next car behind – and so on, until a pile-up occurs.

I conducted a survey, asking people if they knew what the safe stopping distances for cars were at various speeds, and whether they could estimate distances accurately. Many people could not remember the distances and were inaccurate at estimating them. Clearly drivers need to be reminded of these distances and trained to be able to estimate them with reasonable accuracy.

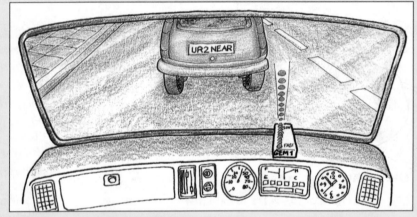

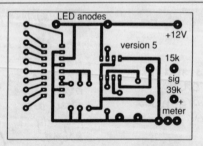

PCB diagram

My idea was to design an LED warning device which would indicate if a driver was too close to the car in front. A row of LEDs would be positioned on the dashboard and reflect onto the windscreen. Depending on the speed the motorist was travelling, if the LED which was lit appeared to be below the back wheel of the car ahead, then they would be in a safe stopping distance.

The system I developed has three basic elements. It starts with a sub-system which creates pulses depending on the

Checking the appropiate distance from the car ahead.

speed. These pulses are turned into a voltage which lights the appropriate LED. To develop this circuit I found some typical application sheets for each of the integrated circuits and produced a circuit diagram which combined the two circuits. I then made it on a bread-board before transferring the design onto a printed-circuit board.

I also produced a polystyrene model of a dashboard to demonstrate the concept. This was replaced later by a vacuum-formed dashboard and further mock-ups using real car dash-boards.

To develop my design further I am working on an automatic switching system and a way of calibrating the system for different driver positions using ergonomic and anthropometric data.